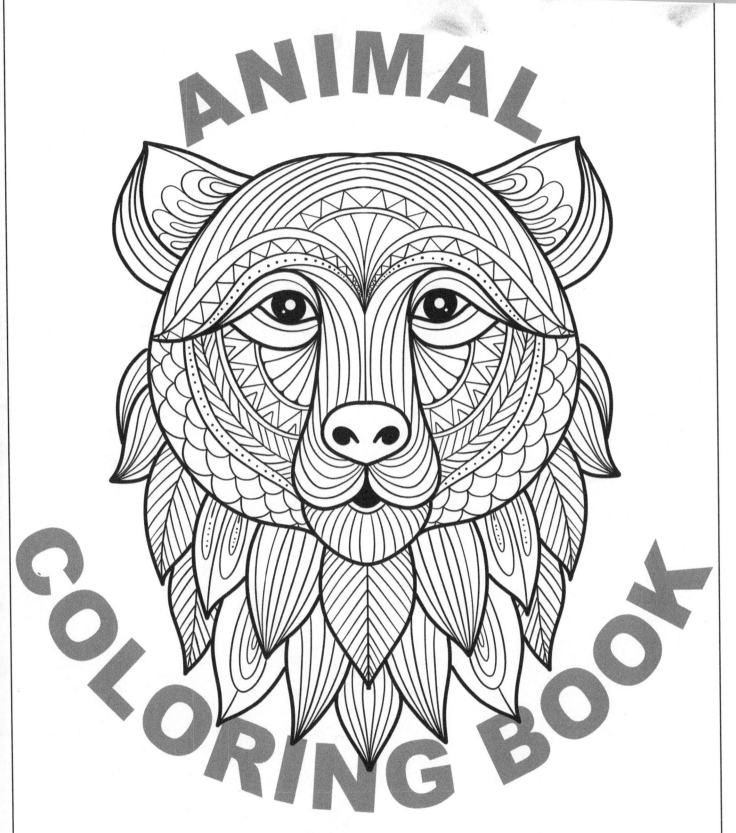

ANIMAL
COLORING BOOK

Welcome to the wonderful world of animals. In this book, you will find some of the fabulous creatures that we share this planet with. All of them play a part in making this world special.

Not all the animals in this book are endangered. Some are, but all of them are affected by our actions. You may live many miles from where they do. You may never even see most of them in your lifetime. But they are there, and they are part of our world.

As you color them in and read a little bit about them, you should begin to understand just how strange and hard life can be. How animals have evolved and adapted to the challenges of living on planet earth.

Could you live in sub-zero temperatures?

Can you run at 30mph for an hour?

Have you gone without food for six months?

It's amazing what some animals have to do to survive. It's fascinating to find out how complex, varied and challenging life can be. We hope you enjoy coloring in these animal mandala designs. We hope that they will also give you something to think about.

Have fun.

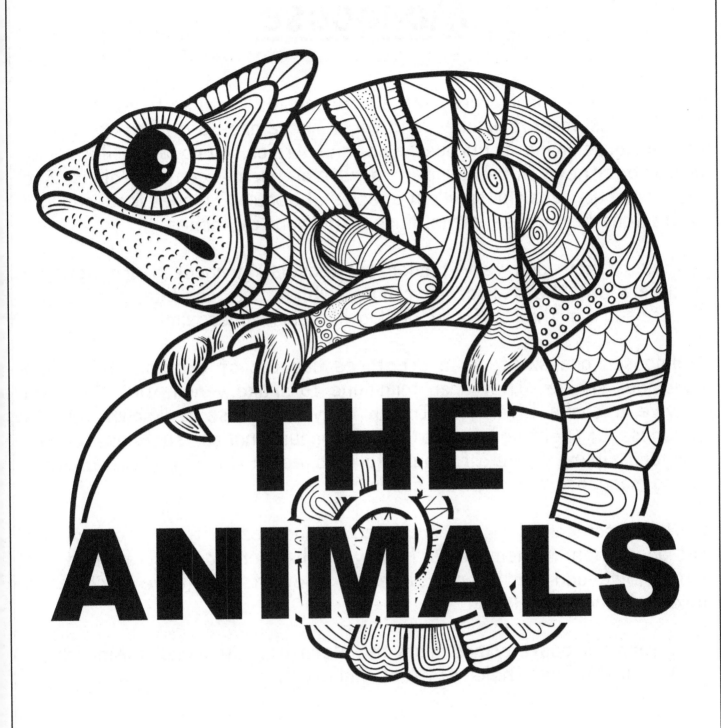

THE
ANIMALS

Mongoose

Mongooses are carnivorous, weasel-like animals that like to eat rodents, birds, frogs, insects, snakes, and eggs. There are 33 different species of mongoose living in Europe, Asia, and Africa. Mongooses like rocky areas, but they can be found in forests and semi-aquatic regions. The dwarf mongoose is the smallest species at about 10 inches long, and the white-tailed mongoose is the biggest at about 30 inches.

Although they look very similar to weasels, mongooses are actually members of the feliforma family, which are cat-like carnivores. Weasels are in the caniforma or dog-like carnivores family.

Mongooses are swift, agile creatures capable of evading and killing venomous snakes. They aren't immune to snake venom, but they can survive a snake bite. The Indian grey mongoose is known for its fondness of fighting and eating poisonous snakes, such as cobras. Rudyard Kipling wrote a famous story called 'Rikki-Tikki-Tavi' about a young mongoose that fights a cobra.

Hawaii sugar cane farmers imported mongooses to try to control the rat population in their fields. However, the mongooses preferred the native bird and turtle populations to the rats and have become an invasive species in Hawaii.

The word mongoose comes from the Marathi name mungūs. Marathi is spoken in the west Indian state of Maharashtra.

Whale

Whales are divided into two main groups. The baleen whales and the toothed whales.

Baleen whales don't have teeth. They have fibrous baleen plates in their mouths which filter out vast quantities of krill, plankton, and crustaceans from the seawater.

Toothed whales have teeth that enable them to feed on larger prey such as fish and squid.

The blue whale is a baleen whale and is the largest animal that has ever lived. It can grow to over 90 feet and weighs 150 tons. Blue whale calves are born weighing 2 tons and drink over 100 gallons of milk every day. They gain 200lbs every day of their first year.

Beluga whales are known as the 'canaries of the sea' because of the sophisticated range of whistles, clicks, and chirps they use to communicate with each other.

Gray whales have the longest annual migration of any mammal. Each year they travel over 10,000 miles from their feeding grounds in the north to their breeding grounds in the south and back.

In 2014, a Cuvier's beaked whale made the deepest and longest dive ever recorded for a whale when it reached a depth of 1.9 miles and stayed submerged for over 2 hours.

Humpback whales don't eat for most of the year. They live off their fat reserves as they migrate from their tropical breeding grounds to the Antarctic to feed on krill.

Some whales catch their prey with bubble nets. This involves them working together and blowing bubbles to encircle their prey. Their prey won't swim through this net of bubbles, making it easy for the whales to catch and eat them.

Whales live in families, known as pods.

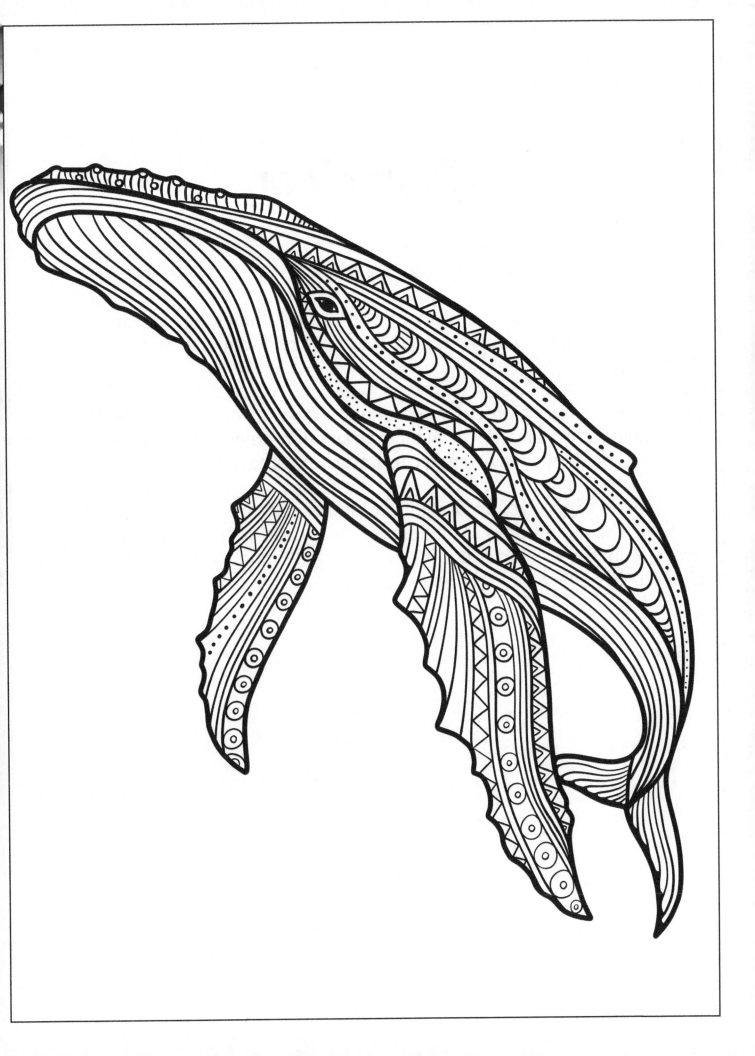

Chameleon

There are around 200 different species of chameleon, almost half of which live in Madagascar. They range in size from $\frac{1}{2}$ inch to as large as 30 inches.

Specialized color pigment cells under the skin called chromatophores allow some chameleons to change their skin color. They mainly change color to communicate or regulate body temperature.

Their eyes can swivel around in two different directions simultaneously to help them find prey. Chameleons eat large insects such as locusts, grasshoppers, crickets, and stick insects. Some of the larger species also eat other lizards and young birds.

Polar Bear

The polar bear is the largest species of bear. A male polar bear can be 10 feet long and weigh over half a ton. Female polar bears are up to 50% smaller than the males. They live in Arctic regions of Russia, Alaska, Canada, Greenland, and Norway. Due to their vast size, they have no natural enemies except humans.

Polar bears live in a freezing environment where the temperature can drop below minus 50°F. They are so well insulated against this cold by a thick layer of blubber and with dense, oily fur that they can quickly overheat when running.

Because they spend most of their lives on sea ice hunting, polar bears are the only bear species to be considered a marine mammal. They are excellent swimmers and have been seen swimming hundreds of miles offshore. They can swim over 100 miles without stopping.

Polar bears have an incredible sense of smell and can smell a seal on the ice over 20 miles away. About half of a polar bear's life is spent hunting, but less than 2% of their hunts are successful. Seals are a polar bear's main prey, but they will also scavenge carcasses or eat small mammals, birds, eggs, and vegetation.

Condor

Condor is the common name for two species of New World vultures. The Andean condor, which lives in the Andean mountains and the California condor, which lives in the western coastal mountains of the United States and Mexico and the northern desert mountains of Arizona in the United States.

The California condor is the largest bird in North America with a wingspan of 10 feet. They are listed as critically endangered, with less than 300 birds left in the wild.

The Andean condor is a slightly shorter bird but has a bigger wingspan and is the largest flying bird in the world by combined measurement of weight and wingspan. It, too, is at risk from habitat loss but is not critically endangered.

Both species of condor fly by gliding on warm air currents and can reach altitudes of 15,000ft. They can travel up to 150 miles per day, searching for food.

Condors get most of their food from carrion, animals that are already dead, and are exposed to all sorts of bacteria. They have a very efficient immune system, so they don't get sick from feeding on decaying animals.

Male and female condors have different color eyes. Females have red eyes, and males have brown.

Komodo Dragon

Komodo dragons are the largest lizard in the world, reaching up to 10 feet in length and weighing 200lbs. They live on four Indonesian islands: Komodo, Flores, Rinca and Gili Motang. They have been around for millions of years but were only discovered in 1910 by Lieutenant van Steyn van Hensbroek who went to Komodo Island after hearing stories about giant lizards.

They are carnivores and will eat pigs, deer, snakes, fish, and water buffalos. Adult Komodo dragons are also cannibals, and 10% of their diet is made of newly hatched Komodo dragons.

Like all reptiles, Komodo dragons smell with their tongues. They have an organ called the Jacobson's Organ in the roof of their mouth. This processes the scent particles on the tongue. Because their tongue is forked, each prong has a different amount of scent on it. This enables to Komodo dragon to not only know what they're smelling but also where it is. They can locate prey up to 4 miles away.

They have highly flexible jaws that they can open very wide and can easily swallow a medium-sized pig in one go. A Komodo dragon can eat as much as 80% of its body weight in one go. That's the same as a person eating about 260 quarter-pound burgers in one go. Because their metabolism is relatively slow and they can eat so much in a single sitting, Komodo dragons can survive on as little as one meal a month.

Komodo dragons are great swimmers. They can swim from one island to another. In fact, they can swim for hours and have been spotted miles offshore

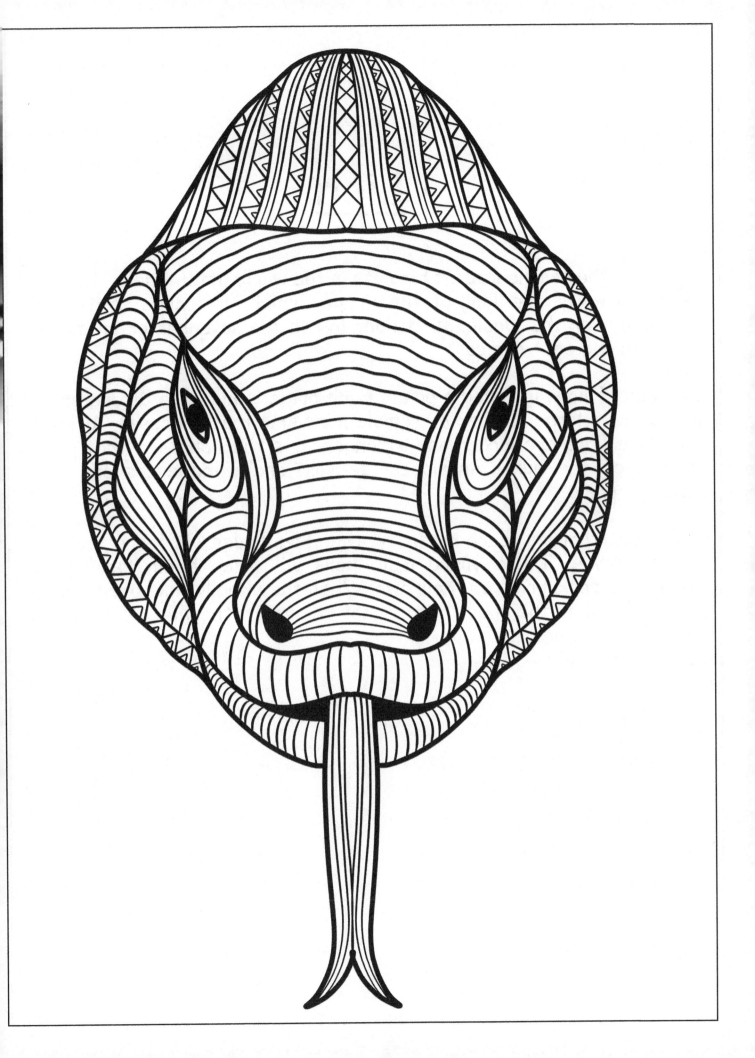

Lion

Lions are the second largest big cats in the world after tigers. They are often known as the 'king of the jungle,' which is strange as they live nowhere near the jungle. Most lions live in the savannah or grasslands of south and east Africa.

A group of lions is called a pride. Each pride is made up of one or two males and a large number of female lions known as lionesses. Although the male lions are larger and stronger, it's the lionesses that are in charge of the hunt. Antelopes, zebras, and wildebeests are their favorite prey.

When young males reach maturity, the older males will force them out of the pride. These young male lions will then begin looking and competing for a pride of their own. When they finally take over a pride, they will kill all the cubs that are not theirs. In the wild, 75% of cubs die at a young age.

Coral

Coral reefs cover less than 1% of the ocean but are home to almost 25% of all known marine species. They are known as the rainforests of the sea.

Coral reefs are among the most biodiverse ecosystems on the planet. There are often more types of fish living in two acres of healthy coral reef than there are species of birds in all of North America.

Coral reefs are the biggest biological structures on earth. Australia's Great Barrier Reef is the largest reef system in the world and can be seen from outer space.

There are three different types of coral reefs. Barrier reefs, coral atolls, and fringing reefs. Barrier reefs help to protect lagoons and other types of shallow water. Coral atolls, which are often mistaken for islands, are made from volcanic remains, and fringing reefs are found all along the coastline.

Although many corals look like plants, they're actually animals and are most closely related to jellyfish and anemones. Coral reefs grow very slowly, at an average rate of just one inch per year. Coral needs sunlight to grow, which is why they thrive in shallow water. They also tend to prefer tropical waters where the sea is warmer and clearer.

Coral reefs help to improve the quality of the surrounding water. They do this by filtering out things floating in the ocean, which leads to cleaner water.

Recent studies suggest the planet has lost approximately half of its coral reefs in the last 30 years and could lose more than 90% by the year 2050 if drastic changes are not made.

Topi

The topi is a medium-sized antelope with a beautiful reddish-brown coat that shimmers in bright sunlight. They have distinct black patches on their face, their upper forelegs, and on their hips and thighs. The topi's tan legs look like they are wearing stockings.

Topis are very sociable animals and live in herds of 15 to 20. However, in some places, it is possible to see herds of hundreds. They can spend a lot of time with other antelopes such as wildebeest and with zebra and ostrich.

The topi is a picky eater. They only eat grass and prefer the most tender shoots. If they have access to green pasture, then they can go without water for a long time. If green grazing is not available, the topic must drink daily.

Topis are one of the fastest antelopes and can reach speeds up to 45mph.

Shark

Sharks live in every ocean on the planet and have done for millions of years. There are almost 500 species of shark, including angel, bullhead, carpet, dogfish, weasel, mackerel, crocodile, zebra, and even catsharks.

The smallest shark is the dwarf lantern that only grows to 6 inches, and the largest is the whale shark that grows to a massive 40 feet in length. The oldest known species of living shark in the goblin shark has been around for 120 million years. The second oldest is the frilled shark that has been around for 80 million years.

Sharks don't deserve their scary reputation. Fewer than 4 people a year are killed by sharks. Humans kill 100 million sharks a year. For every single person killed by a shark, humans kill 25 million sharks.

There are plenty of animals that are far more dangerous than sharks. Hippos kill nearly 3,000 people a year in Africa every year. Deer are responsible for 130 deaths per year, usually due to car collisions, and cows kill about 22 people a year.

Sharks have an incredible sense of smell. A great white shark can detect one drop of blood in half a million gallons of water. That's one drop in an Olympic size swimming pool.

Sharks can also detect prey by the small electrical fields that all animals generate. They have tiny organs called the ampullae of Lorenzini located near their nostrils, around their head and beneath their snout, which can sense animals around them.

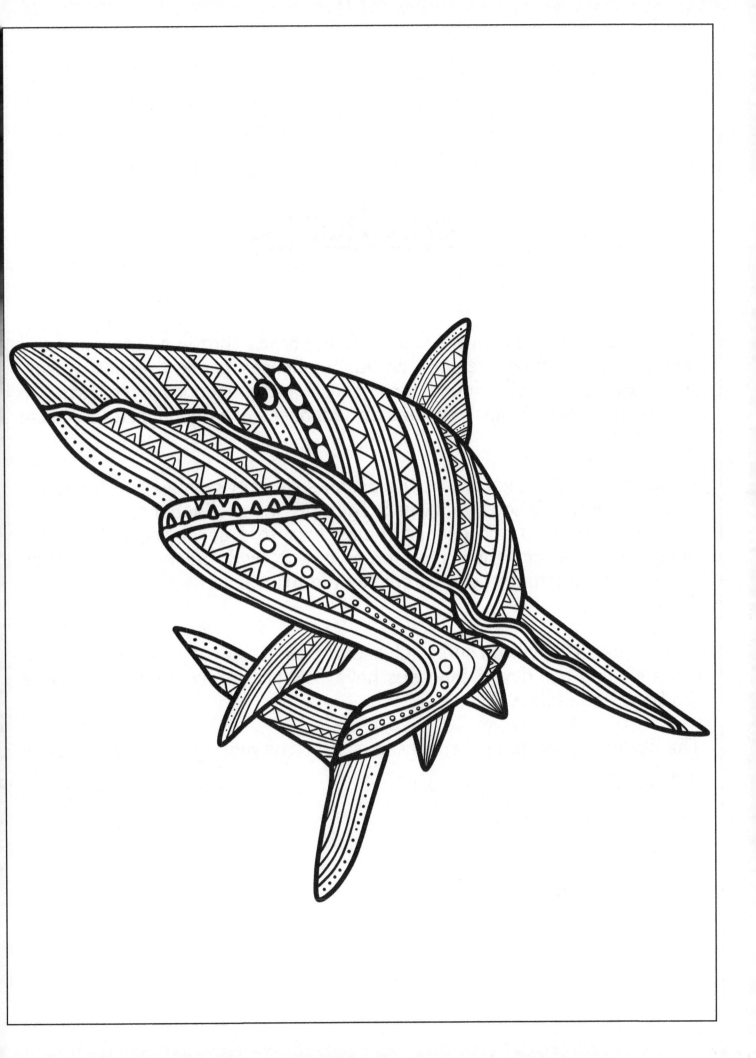

Seahorse

There are about 40 known species of seahorses that live in tropical and temperate water all over the world. Seahorses prefer shallow water, and they are usually found near coral reefs, mangrove forests, or clumps of seaweed. Many species of seahorses are endangered because of overfishing.

Seahorses hold the record as the ocean's slowest swimmers. The dwarf seahorse only manages to swim 5 feet per hour. Seahorses use their tails to grab on to and anchor themselves to a coral branch or some seaweed to prevent them from being swept away. Seahorses are such weak swimmers that they can quickly die of exhaustion when caught in stormy seas.

Seahorses eat plankton and small crustaceans. They can eat up to 3,000 brine shrimp per day. Seahorses have few predators because they're too bony and indigestible.

The oddest thing about seahorses is that the male gives birth to baby seahorses.

Butterfly

There are about 24,000 species of butterflies ranging in size from $\frac{1}{2}$ inch to 12 inches. Butterflies belong to the Lepidoptera class of insects, which are characterized by their large scaly wings. Antarctica is the only continent on which no Lepidoptera are found.

Monarch butterflies journey on one of nature's great migrations. In the autumn, they travel 2,000 miles from their breeding grounds in the Great Lakes of North America to the warmer mountains of central Mexico.

The Brimstone butterfly is the longest living butterfly with a lifespan of 10 months. However, most butterflies only live for a few weeks.

Butterflies feed on nectar from flowers, but they need minerals too. To supplement their diet of nectar, a butterfly will occasionally sip from mud puddles, which are rich in minerals and salts.

A butterfly's eyes are made up of over 6,000 individual lenses, and they can see beyond the ultraviolet spectrum.

A group of butterflies is known as a flutter.

Tasmanian Devil

Tasmanian devils are the world's largest marsupial carnivore. They are only found on the island of Tasmania in Australia.

Their oversized heads have incredibly strong jaws that can open very wide and deliver the strongest bite for its size of any mammal in the world. They have the power to bite through thick metal wire.

Tasmanian devils grow to the size of a small dog, and, like a dog, they have 42 teeth. Unlike a dog, a Tasmanian devil's teeth grow continuously throughout its life, contributing to its phenomenal ability to consume the bones of its prey. Tasmanian devils can eat up to 10% of their body weight in a day.

Tasmanian devils are not very fast runners, but they can run for a long time without resting. They are excellent climbers and swimmers.

Like all marsupials, Tasmanian devils store fat in their tails, which thicken up just like a humans' waistline.

European settlers called them devils after their loud and scary growls and screams, which they make during the twilight hours.

Raccoon

Raccoons are smaller relatives of bears and are native to South and North America. They are omnivores and will eat insects, eggs, small mammals, fruit, berries, seed, rubbish, in fact, just about anything. They are excellent swimmers and climbers.

Raccoons have some of the most dexterous hands in nature. The name raccoon comes from the Native American Powhatan people's word aroughcun, which means 'animal that scratches with its hands.' The Aztecs called the raccoon mapachito or 'one who takes everything in its hands.' The Spanish word for raccoon is mapache.

Their famous black masks might make raccoons look like outlaws, but they also help them see clearly. During the day, the black fur reduces sun glare. At night, when raccoons are most active, the black fur reduces peripheral light, which improves their night vision.

Most animals use either sight, sound, or smell for hunting, raccoons rely on their sense of touch. Their front paws contain four times more nerves than their back paws. This allows them to differentiate between objects without seeing them, which is really important when feeding at night.

Raccoons heighten their sense of touch through dowsing. This looks like the animals are washing their food, but what they're really doing is wetting their paws to stimulate the nerve endings.

Raccoons are about as big as small dogs, and a group of raccoons is called a gaze of raccoons.

Pangolin

There are eight different species of pangolins. Four of them live in Asia and four in Africa. Pangolins are the only mammal in the world to be covered in scales. Their body is covered with hard, brown scales made of keratin, which is the same substance that human nails and hair are made of. Scales cover every piece of their body except their forehead, belly, and the inner side of their legs.

Pangolins are insectivores, meaning they only eat insects, and they have very long sticky tongues. Pangolins use their tongues to collect termites. They poke their long, sticky tongues into termite mounds and gather up the termites.

Pangolins can eat up to 70 million insects per year. They do not have teeth, so they swallow sand and small stones along with the insects to help grind up their food.

The name pangolin is derived from the Malay word 'pengguling,' which means 'rolling up' because of the pangolin's defense mechanism. It rolls up into a tight, hard ball when under threat. Even lions won't bother with a rolled-up pangolin.

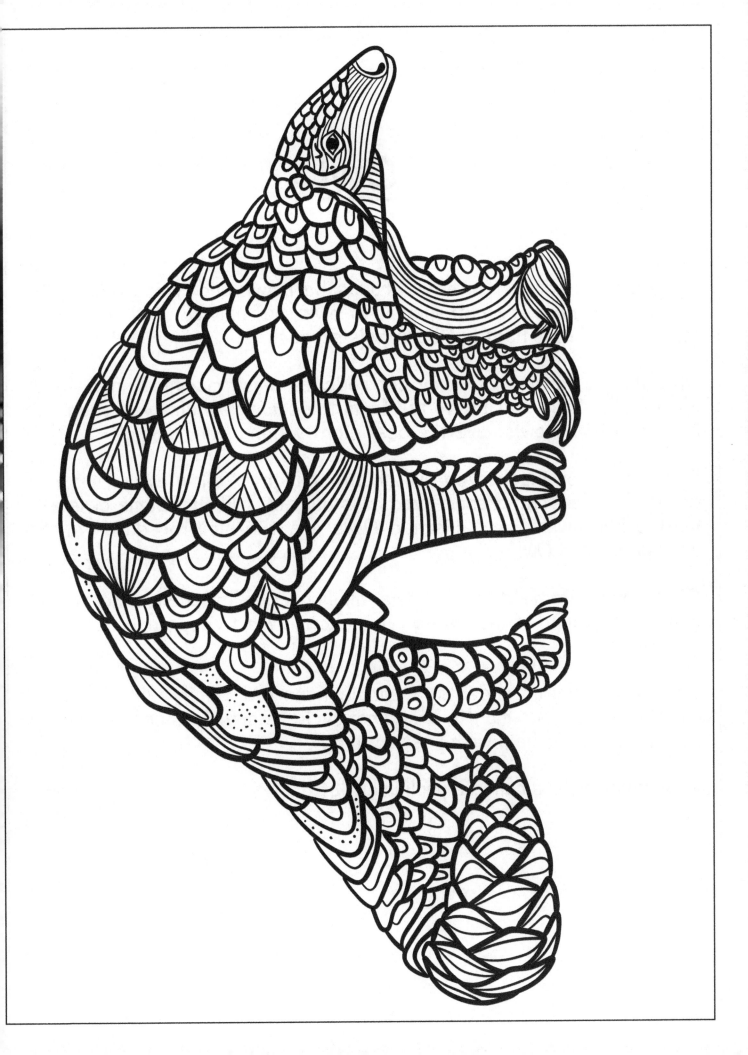

Owl

All owls can be divided into two groups: barn owls and typical (also called true) owls. There are 225 species of owls, but only 18 of them of barn owls. Typical owls hoot but barn owls screech.

All owls are carnivores. They eat rodents, small mammals, fish, birds, and insects. It is possible to tell from the color of their eyes when they hunt. Nocturnal owls have the best night vision of any animal.

Dark brown or black-eyed owls hunt at night. Yellow-eyed owls hunt during the day, and orange-eyed owls hunt at twilight. Some owls even hunt other owls. Great Horned Owls are the main predator of the smaller Barred Owl.

Owls have soft feathers on the trailing edge of their wing to help muffle the sound of the flying. This allows owls to approach their prey unnoticed.

Owls eat a lot of rodents. A single barn owl family will eat 3,000 rodents in a four-month breeding cycle. Many farmers install owl nesting boxes to help with pest control.

A group of owls is called a parliament of owls.

Peacock

A peacock is the male peafowl bird. A peahen is the female bird, and the chicks are called peachicks. Peafowl are native to Asia and belong to the pheasant family. There are two species of peafowl: Indian Peafowl and Green Peafowl.

Peafowl are omnivores. They eat insects, reptiles, amphibians, flowers and seeds.

Peacocks have a relatively large wingspan of around 5 feet, which makes them one of the biggest flying birds on earth. Their large colorful tails are called a train.

Peahens lay unfertilized eggs as decoys in places far away from their nest to confuse predators that might steal them.

A group of peacocks is called an ostentation of peacocks.

In Hindu culture, Lord Karthikeya, the god of war, is said to ride a peacock.

Markhor

The markhor is a type of wild goat and the largest member of the goat family. The name markhor means snake in Persian and probably refers to the shape of their horns, although they are known to be able to kill snakes.

There are three species of markhor. The flare-horned markhor, the straight-horned markhor, and the Bukharan markhor. The male markhor's horns can reach 5 feet in length.

Markhors live at high altitudes in the mountains of Pakistan, Afghanistan, and India. Their natural enemies are lynx, snow leopards, wolves, and black bears. Markhors are fantastic climbers and will use their climbing skills to try and escape any predators. They are known for smelling really, really bad, especially the males. People will often smell them long before actually seeing them.

Markhors are the national animal of Pakistan.

<u>Octopus</u>

There are over 300 species of octopuses living in the oceans of the world, usually near coral reefs. Octopuses are invertebrates, so they have no bones, but they do have a hard beak, which they use for eating. They like to eat crabs, mollusks, and crayfish. At less than an inch long, the wolfi octopus is the smallest while the giant Pacific octopus is the largest at over 16 feet.

Most people think that octopuses have eight tentacles, but that's wrong. Octopuses have eight arms. Tentacles are for squid, cuttlefish, and nautiluses.

Most of an octopus's neurons are in its arms, which means they can act independently of each other. One arm can be exploring a cave while another opens a clam.

Octopuses are highly intelligent and are capable of solving puzzles and distinguishing shapes and patterns.

Octopuses have three hearts, blue blood, and the ability to change the color and texture of their skin in just three-tenths of a second. This helps them blend in with their environment and become invisible.

One of their hearts pumps blood through its organs; the other two pump blood through its gills. Their blood is blue because it has a copper-based protein called hemocyanin. This copper base is more efficient at transporting oxygen than iron-based hemoglobin when the water temperature is very low, and not much oxygen is around.

Unfortunately, the copper base also causes them to be extremely sensitive to changes in acidity. As the climate changes and the oceans become more acidic, octopuses are more at risk.

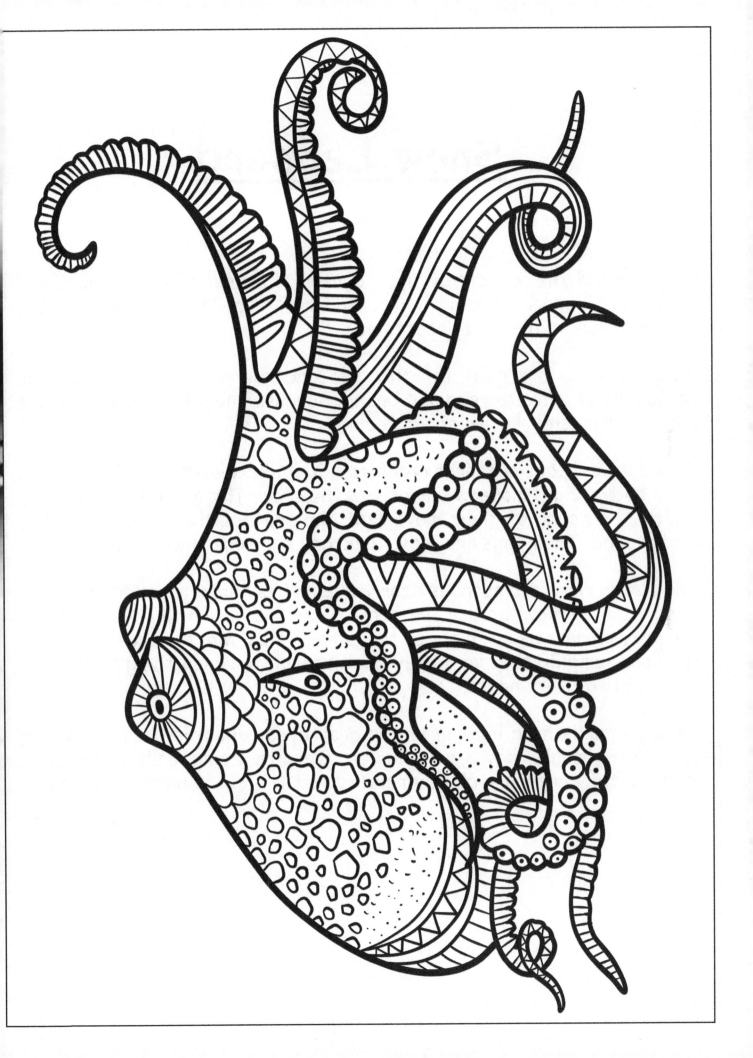

Snow Leopard

Often called the 'ghosts of the mountain' because they are so rarely seen, snow leopards live in the mountains of Asia. They are the only big cats that live in the cold deserts of Asia.

Snow leopards are built for the cold and spend their lives crossing thousands of miles to feed and breed. Because they live in such remote areas, not much is known about them.

Snow leopard paws are large and furry, just like snowshoes, that spread their body weight more evenly across the snow. The giant paws also help muffle the sound of their movement and protect their toes from the cold ground. Their tails are very thick, and they use them as a fat store.

The fur on their stomachs is nearly five inches thick, which keeps them warm as they move across the snow. They are powerful creatures and can prey on animals up to three times their size. Most impressive of all, they can jump 20 feet vertically, high enough to reach the gutter on an average two-story house.

Snow leopards have light green or grey eyes, which is unusual for big cats, who usually have yellow eyes. Despite being called the snow leopard, they are more closely related to the tiger than the leopard.

Giraffe

Giraffes are the tallest mammals on Earth. Their legs alone are 6 feet tall, which is taller than most humans. Despite being incredibly tall, giraffes still only have seven vertebrae in their necks, the same number of vertebrae as in a human's neck. They can run as fast as 35mph over short distances, or canter at 10mph over longer distances.

Giraffes spend most of their lives standing up. They even sleep and give birth standing up. Giraffes only need 5 to 30 minutes of sleep every 24 hours, which they often get in quick naps lasting only a minute or two at a time.

Because of their unusual shape, giraffes have a highly specialized cardiovascular system. Their heart is two feet long and weighs 11 kgs, making it the biggest heart of any land mammal. It pumps 14 gallons of blood around the body every minute at a blood pressure twice that of an average human.

Giraffes are herbivores, but their enormous skeletons require more calcium and phosphorus than they can get from a diet of just plants. To make up the deficiency, they chew on bones from carcasses that they come across. This behavior is known as osteophagy.

The giraffe's scientific name, Giraffa camelopardalis, comes from the ancient Greeks' belief that it looked like a camel wearing a leopard's coat.

A group of giraffes is called a tower of giraffes.

Caribou

There are two species of caribou. The tundra caribou and the woodland caribou. Caribou and reindeer are different names for the same animal. North Americans call them caribou, and northern Europeans call them reindeer.

Caribou are ungulates meaning they have hooves. Their hooves change with the seasons. In summer, their hoof pads are thick and spongy for walking on softer ground. In winter, their hooves shrink and become harder, which is better for scraping ice and also reduces contact with the cold ground. They are the only member of the deer family where both males and females have antlers.

Wild Caribou live in large, migratory herds of between 100 and 250,000 individuals and can run as fast as 30mph. They travel up to 3,000 miles each year in their search for food, and although they are a large animal, they also have a lot of predators. Wolves, bears, lynx, wolverines, and golden eagles all like to eat caribou.

Caribou have two layers of fur. The bottom layer is a very fine, dense hair while the outer shaggier layer is made up of hollow insulating hairs that help keep them warm.

Caribou can see ultraviolet light, which means they can see even during the winter months when the sun doesn't shine. When it is dark and snowy, it can be hard for them to keep track of each other. They have tendons that slip over bones in their feet as they walk, producing a loud clicking sound, which helps them to stay together.

The Mi'Kmaq are an indigenous first nations people in Canada. The name 'Caribou' comes from the Mi'Kmaq word 'qalipu' (pronounced: KAL-i-bu), which means 'one who paws.' Caribou use their hooves to paw snow away from the plants underneath.

Platypus

The platypus is native to Eastern Australia and Tasmania and is the strangest mammal in the world. It is duck-billed, has a beaver-like tail, lays eggs, has otter-like fur and webbed feet, and the male platypus has venomous ankle spurs.

When Europeans first encountered the platypus, many believed the animal was a hoax. They thought it was a beaver's body sewn together with a duck's bill as some sort of joke.

Platypuses and echidnas are the only two mammals in the world classed as monotremes, which means that they lay eggs instead of giving birth to live offspring. Females platypus lay 2-4 eggs, incubating them for two weeks.

A platypus's bill contains thousands of nerve cells that allow them to detect the electric fields generated by all living things. It's so sensitive that the platypus can hunt with its eyes, ears, and nose all closed, relying entirely on the bill's electrolocation to find its prey.

Male platypuses have venomous stingers above the heel of the rear feet for protection against predators. The venom is powerful enough to kill small dogs, and although it is not lethal to humans, it can cause severe pain that lasts for weeks.

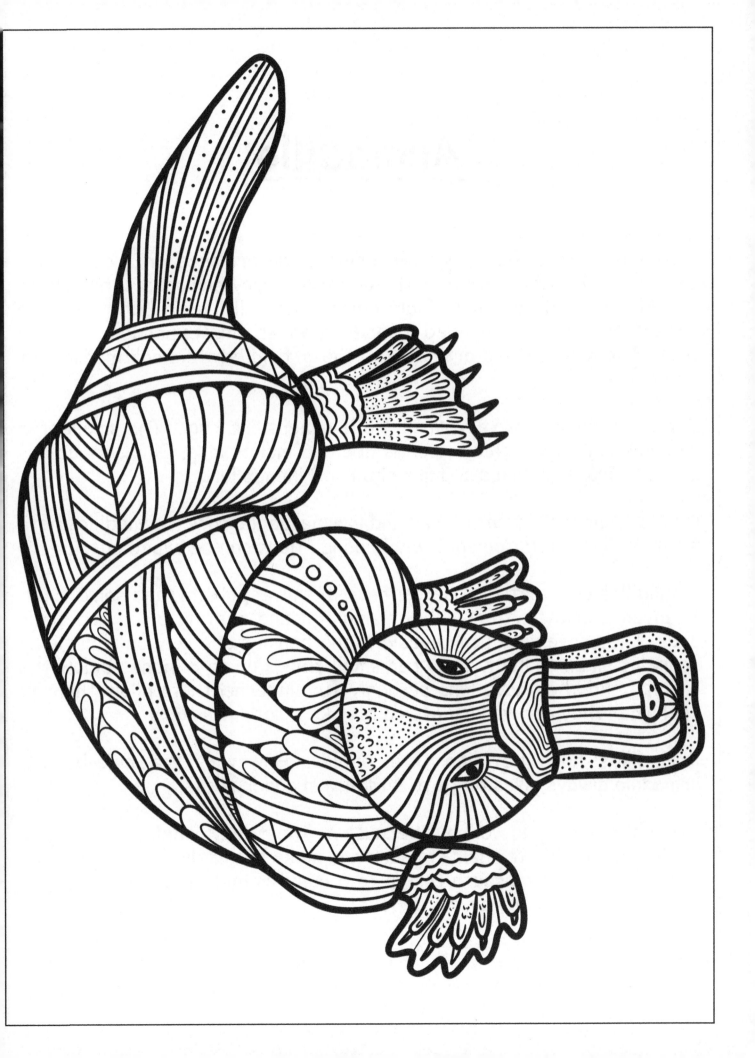

Armadillo

Translated from the Spanish meaning 'little armored one', armadillos are the only living mammal with such a leathery armored shell. There are 21 different species of armadillo. They all live in Latin America except for the nine-banded armadillo, which has expanded into the USA. The nine-banded armadillo is the official state small mammal of Texas.

Some armadillos are very small, while others are huge. The smallest is the pink fairy armadillo, which is about 6 inches long. Giant armadillos are the largest species and are about 60 inches long.

Due to their lack of fat stores and low metabolic rates, armadillos hate the cold. If it gets too cold, whole populations can be wiped out.

Armadillos eat beetles, insects, ants, termites, plants, and some fruit. If given a chance, they will eat small ground-nesting birds and their eggs. They have very poor eyesight and hearing and rely on their keen sense of smell to hunt. They can smell things up to 8 inches below the ground, and they have long scraggly fur underneath to allow them to feel what they are walking over a bit like a cat's whiskers.

Armadillos have between 1-15 babies. However, the nine-banded armadillo always gives birth to 4 identical quadruplets.

Armadillos can swim well, but because of their heavy shell, they have to swallow air to inflate their stomach and make themselves buoyant. They can also hold their breath for up to 6 minutes and will sometimes walk across the bottom of a river or lake.

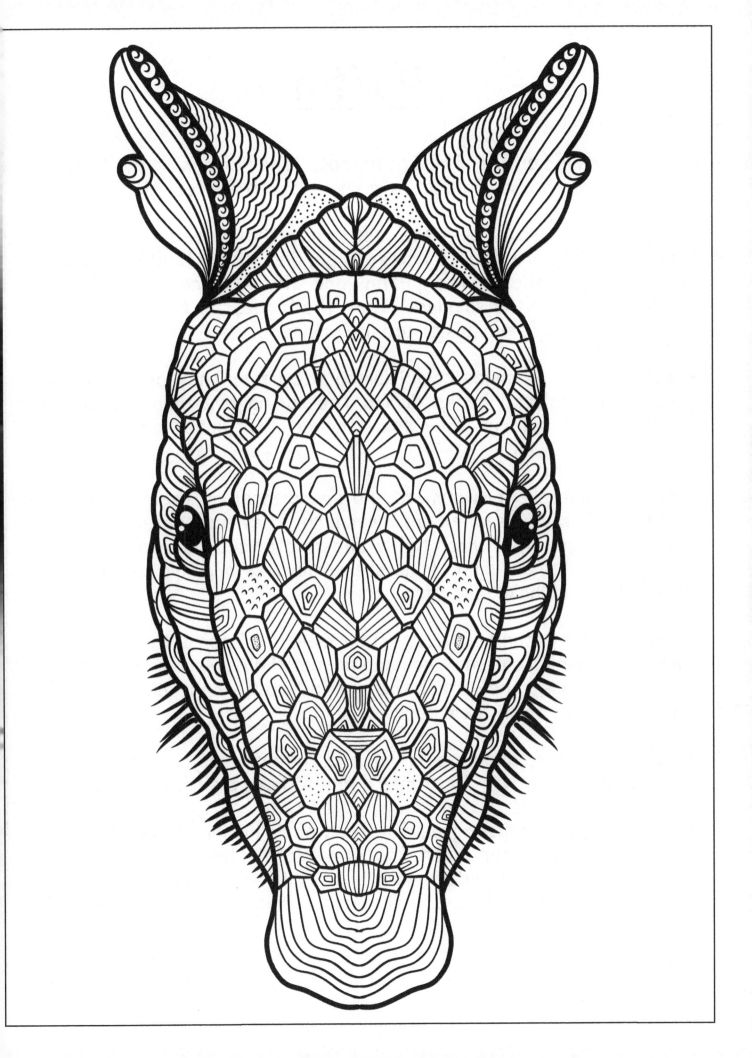

Puffin

Commonly called either 'The Sea Parrot,' 'The Penguin of the North,' or 'The Clown of the Sea,' puffins are known for their technicolor beaks.

The puffin is a seabird in the auk family that breeds in and around Iceland. There are four species of puffins: the Atlantic puffin, the horned puffin, the tufted puffin, and the Rhinoceros Auklet. The Atlantic puffin is the smallest, while the biggest is the tufted puffin. 60% of the world's puffins breed in Iceland.

A puffin's beak changes color during the year. They only have their bright multi-colored beaks during the spring breeding season. Just before winter sets in, they shed the colorful outer beak, leaving a smaller, duller beak.

Puffins are excellent swimmers and spend most of their lives at sea, resting on the waves when not swimming. They only return to land to breed. They use their wings to 'fly' underwater and can reach depths of 200 feet while hunting. Puffins are carnivores and live off small fish such as herring, hake, and sand eels.

Puffins live for around 20 years. Their main predator is the great black-backed gull, which can capture a puffin mid-flight. Herring gulls are also a threat because they steal the puffins' catch and pull the puffins' chicks and eggs from their burrows.

A young puffin is called a puffling, and they're hungry animals. Parent birds have to dive over 200 times a day to feed a single puffling.

Puffins are not the most graceful flying birds having to flap their wings 300 to 400 times per minute to stay aloft. They also have trouble landing, often crashing into the water or rolling onto the grass, tumbling into other puffins that are in the way. Puffins cannot fly unless they have a view of the ocean.

Bison

Bison are the largest North American mammal. Male bison can weigh up to a ton and stand 6 feet tall, while females weigh up to half a ton and reach a height of 4-5 feet.

Yellowstone National Park in the U.S.A. is the only place in the world where bison have continuously lived since prehistoric times. What makes Yellowstone's bison so unique is that they are free of modern cattle genes. They are the pure descendants of bison that roamed America's grasslands before modern humans evolved.

They may be big, weighing nearly a ton, but bison are also fast and can run up to 35mph. Plus, they're incredibly agile. Bison can spin around quickly, jump high fences, and are strong swimmers.

Bison are herbivores, which means they only eat vegetation. Typically, grass and herbs, but they will also eat leaves and twigs.

During the 19th century, American settlers killed some 50 million bison for food, sport, and to deprive Native Americans of their most valuable natural asset.

Kangaroo

Kangaroos are marsupials. These are animals with pouches in which the young finish their development after birth.

There are four species of kangaroo. The red kangaroo, the antilopine kangaroo, the eastern grey kangaroo, and the western grey kangaroo. The eastern grey is the heaviest at 200lbs, and the red kangaroo is the tallest at 9 feet. They live in Australia and New Guinea and can be found in different types of habitats, including open scrublands, grasslands, woodlands, and deserts.

Kangaroos come from a family of animals called macropods, which means 'large foot.' Kangaroos are the biggest macropods. Other macropods are wallabies and wallaroos, which are in between wallabies and kangaroos in size.

Young kangaroos are called joeys, but the adult females can be called does, flyers or jills, and the males are called bucks, boomers, or jacks.

Kangaroos are very social animals and live in groups that can be called a troop, a mob, or a herd of kangaroos. Male kangaroos can leap 30 feet along the ground and 10 feet in height, and they can reach speeds of 40mph.

There are more kangaroos than humans in Australia.

Jaguar

The jaguar is the third-largest big cat in the world, but it is the largest cat in the Americas. It can be found in North, Central, and South America in a wide variety of ecosystems such as rainforests, swamps, grasslands, scrub woodlands, and forests.

The name jaguar is derived from the Native American word 'yaguar' which means 'he who kills in a single leap.'

Jaguars have the most powerful bite of any big cat. Their teeth are strong enough to bite through the thick hides of crocodiles and the hard shells of turtles. Jaguars are carnivores, but they do eat avocados occasionally.

They are excellent climbers and often drag their food up trees for safekeeping. They also use their vantage point among the branches to pounce on unsuspecting prey below.

Jaguars can be melanistic, where they appear almost black. Melanistic jaguars are known as 'black panthers.' Unlike most cats, jaguars like to spend time in the water, and they are excellent swimmers.

The Anaconda is the only natural enemy of the jaguar.

<u>Woodpecker</u>

There are more than 180 species of woodpeckers worldwide, and they can be found in forests, deserts, jungles, and even urban settings. There are no woodpeckers in Australia, Madagascar, New Zealand, or Antarctica.

The largest woodpecker, the great slaty woodpecker, can reach 20 inches in length. The smallest woodpeckers, the piculets, are only 4 inches long.

Woodpeckers are usually red, white, black, and yellow, but their plumage can also be a combination of orange, green, brown, and gold.

Woodpeckers are omnivores. They will eat insects, insect larvae and eggs, tree sap, seeds, and nuts. They have a very long tongue, which is designed to dig foot from inside trees. Certain species even have barbed tongues.

A woodpecker can peck 20 times per second and up to 12,000 times per day. All that pecking doesn't hurt them as they have a specially designed skull with air pockets and extra muscles to protect their brain.

Woodpeckers are easy to spot when flying. They always flap their wings three times, followed by a glide. They repeat this pattern all the time while flying.

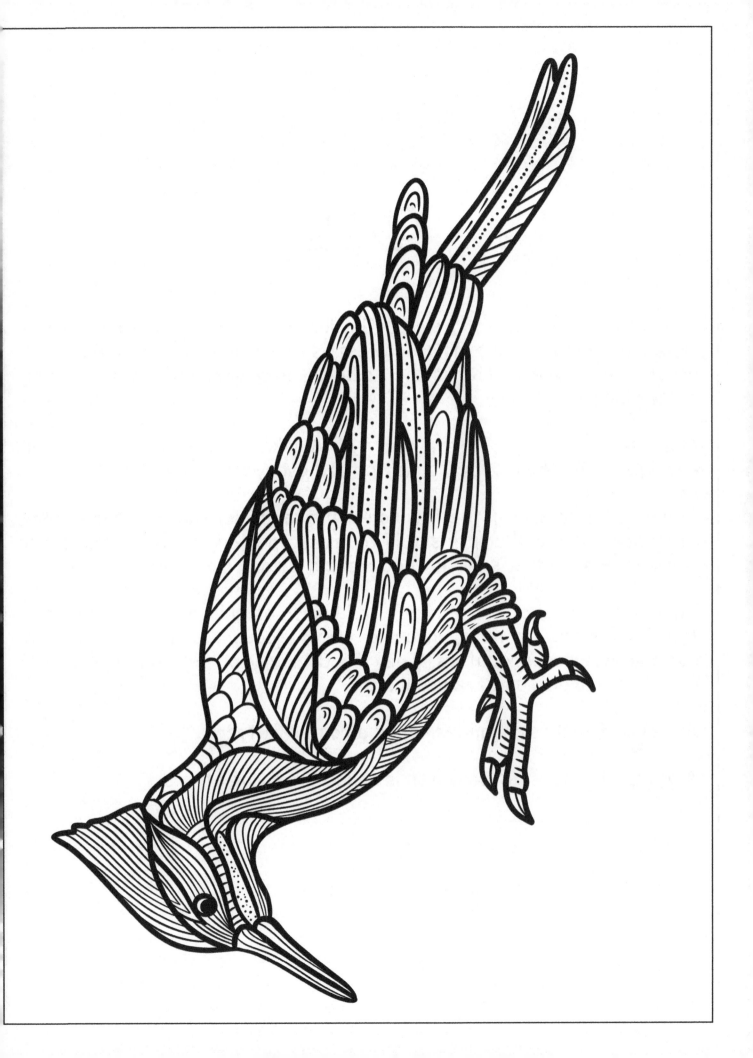

Otter

There are 13 species of otters. The largest is the giant otter, which grows to about 5 feet. The heaviest is the sea otter weighing up to 90lbs. The smallest otter is the Asian small-clawed otter, which is only 3 feet long.

Most sea otters live on the coast of Alaska. They're hungry animals eating 25% of their body weight in food every day.

Sea otters are one of the few non-primate animals known to use tools. They use rocks and empty shells to crack open crabs, sea urchins, and mussels. A sea otter's fur is the thickest of any mammal.

The giant otters of the Amazon are known as ariranha in Brazil, from the Tupí word ari'raña, meaning water jaguar, and reflects their position as apex predators. They feed mainly on fish but will attack crabs, anacondas, and even caimans.

A group of otters on land is called a romp of otters.

A group of otters in the water is called a raft of otters.

Ostrich

Ostriches are the largest and heaviest birds in the world. They can't fly, but they can sprint at up to 40mph and run for long distances at over 30mph. They have powerful legs, and one kick can kill a lion.

The scientific name for an ostrich is Camelus, and it was once known as the 'camel bird.' Like camels, the ostrich can tolerate high temperatures and go without water for long periods.

Males ostriches are black and white color while females and young are usually grey, brown, and white. They are omnivorous and typically eat plants, roots, and seeds but will also eat insects and small lizards.

They live in herds of about ten birds and lay their eggs in one big communal nest. Their eggs are the biggest of any bird. However, in relation to the size of the ostrich, they are actually small compared to other birds.

Newly hatched chicks are about the size of a chicken, but they grow at a rate of 12 inches per month, and by 6 months of age, they are nearly as large as their parents.

Orca

Orcas, or killer whales, aren't actually whales. They're as large as some whales, but they're actually the world's biggest species of dolphin.

Orcas have a very distinctive black and white appearance and live in every ocean ranging from the Arctic to the Antarctic. With their large size and immense power, orcas are quick swimmers and have been recorded at speeds of up to 33mph.

A group of orcas is known as a pod. A pod usually consists of a mature female, her adult offspring, and her daughters' offspring. Older female orcas will help to guide and care for young members of the pod.

As a top predator, they hunt everything. Fish, walruses, seals, sea lions, penguins, squid, sea turtles, sharks, and even other kinds of whales are all on their menu, and they eat about 500lbs of food a day.

Orcas swim up to 40 miles a day and dive to depths of 500 feet several times a day foraging for food. Although killer whales do not migrate, they have been known to travel hundreds of miles to find food that is in 'season.'

Arctic Fox

The Arctic fox is the smallest member of the canine family. There are 5 subspecies of Arctic fox, and they all inhabit tundra throughout the Arctic Circle. The Arctic fox can be found in Iceland, Greenland, Northern Europe, Russia, Canada, and Alaska.

The Arctic fox has the warmest fur of any animal found in the Arctic, enduring temperatures as low as -58°F. They were overhunted in the past because of their beautiful, warm pelts.

The Latin name for the Arctic fox is 'Vulpes Lagopus,' meaning hare-footed fox. This is because of the fur they have on their paws, which reduces heat loss and enables them to walk better on ice.

Their thick fur enables them to maintain consistent body temperature and provides excellent insulation. Their short legs, short muzzle, and rounded ears all reduce the amount of surface area for heat loss.

Arctic foxes are omnivores. The majority of their diet is made up of small mammals, including lemmings, voles, and hares. Lemmings are their favorite, and Arctic fox populations can vary depending on lemming numbers. They will also follow polar bears and wolves around, scavenging their leftovers. In summer months, when food is scarce, they will eat berries and store food in their dens to keep for later.

The Arctic fox is the only land mammal native to Iceland. It came to the isolated North Atlantic island at the end of the last ice age, walking over the frozen sea.

Arctic foxes are active all year round and do not hibernate.

Flamingo

Flamingos live in the shallow lakes, mangrove swamps, and sandy islands of Africa, Asia, America, and Europe. The word 'flamingo' comes from the Spanish word 'flamenco,' meaning fire, which refers to the bright pink or orange color of the feathers.

The color of their feathers is a result of the food they eat. Shrimp, algae, and crustaceans have a pigment called carotenoid in them, and it is this that makes the flamingos pink.

There are 6 species of flamingos. The greater flamingo, Chilean flamingo, lesser flamingo, Caribbean flamingo, Andean flamingo, and puna flamingos.

Flamingos live in large groups called colonies that can consist of millions of birds. Flamingos use these enormous flocks as a safety measure against predators. Larger flocks are also more stable for population growth and breeding success.

A colony of flamingos can also be called a stand or a flamboyance of flamingos.

Panda

Panda bears are the only bear that doesn't hibernate. Their bamboo diet is so nutritionally poor that they can't put on enough fat reserves for hibernation. They spend up to 14 hours a day eating and can eat up to 80lbs of bamboo a day.

The panda's face looks chubby, but it's not fat. The shape is due to the massive cheek muscles needed to bite through thick bamboo stalks. Pandas can bite through bamboo, so thick people would need an ax to cut through it.

Panda bears have a 'thumb,' which is actually an extra-large wrist bone, just for holding onto bamboo stalks.

Scientists are not sure why a panda's fur is colored in such a unique way, even the color of the skin matches. The skin is black under the black fur and pink under the white fur.

It is very rare to see more than one panda at a time in the wild. Giant pandas cannot afford the energy it would take to compete with one another for food, territory, and mates, so they live very solitary lives.

Elephant

There are three different species of elephants. The African Savannah elephant, the African forest elephant, and the Asian elephant.

Elephants are the world's largest land animal. Male African elephants can reach 10 feet tall and weigh up to 7 tons. Asian elephants are slightly smaller, reaching 9 feet tall and weighing up to 6 tons. They are well-known for living in matriarchal, female-led, herds, and they are the only mammal that can't jump.

African elephants have large ears shaped like the continent of Africa. Asian elephants' ears are smaller and shaped like India.

An elephant's trunk is its most important limb. Their trunk is sensitive enough to pick up a blade of grass and strong enough to rip the branches off a tree. Their trunk is also used for drinking. An elephant can suck up to 3 gallons of water at a time and then blow it straight into its mouth. Elephants are excellent swimmers and use their trunk as a snorkel underwater.

Elephants are intelligent animals and have wonderful memories. Matriarchs, in charge of the herd, rely on their memory during dry seasons when they need to guide their herds, sometimes for tens of miles, to watering holes that they remember from the past.

Around 90% of African elephants have been wiped out in the past century, mainly due to the ivory trade.

Alligator

There are two different types of alligator. The American alligator is the larger of the two and can grow up to 12 feet long and weigh nearly half a ton. The smaller Chinese alligator grows to about 5 feet long and is much lighter at about 55lbs.

The American alligator is the largest reptile in North America. They live in freshwater wetlands in the southeastern United States. They have one of the most powerful bites of any animal and can consume almost a quarter of their body weight in one meal. Their teeth are constantly being replaced as they wear down and fall out. An alligator can go through 2,000 teeth in its lifetime.

Alligators have existed since around the time the dinosaurs went extinct. The word 'alligator' comes from the Spanish word 'el lagarto,' which means 'the lizard.'

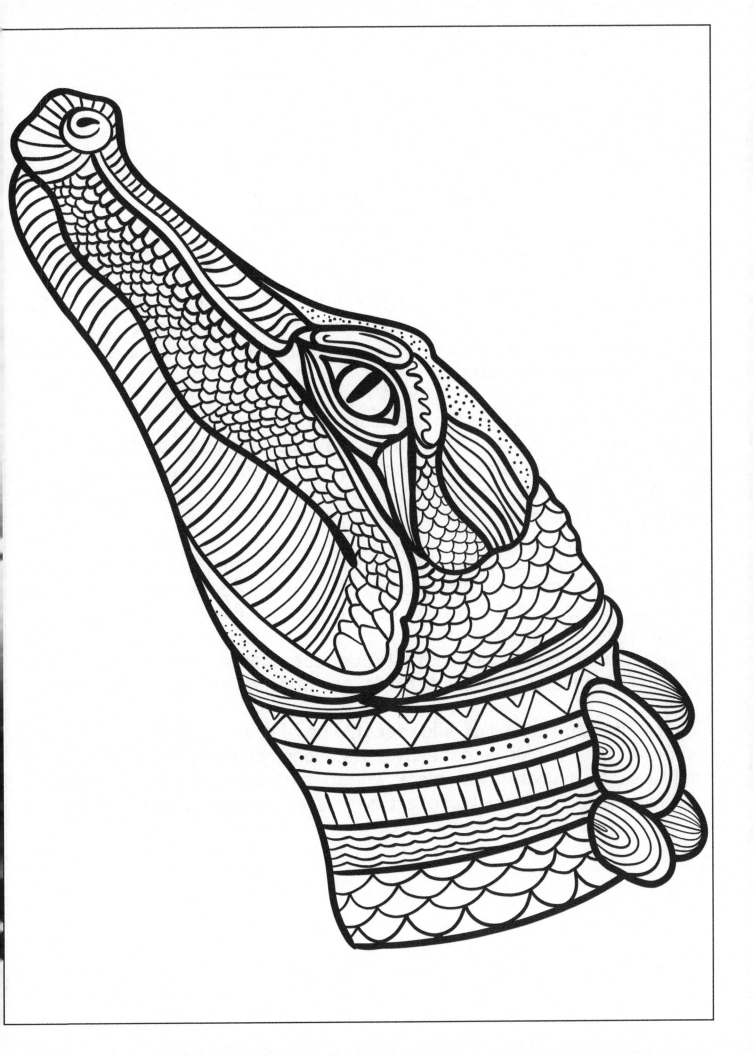

Wildebeest

Wildebeests, also known as gnu, are one of the largest antelopes. They can reach 8 feet in length, 5 feet in height and weigh over 600lbs. They live on the green plains and open woodlands of central, eastern, and southern parts of Africa.

Vast herds of wildebeest migrate across Africa in May and June every year. Traveling up to 1000 miles a day, accompanied by hundreds of thousands of associated animals, such as zebras and Thompson's gazelles. The great migration is one of Africa's most spectacular natural phenomena.

Zebra and wildebeest have a symbiotic relationship. Zebras feed on the long, tough grasses on the plains, while the wildebeests feed on the shorter grasses. Also, zebras have a great memory that helps them recall safe migration routes, which comes in handy for directing the sometimes aimless wildebeests. Wildebeests, on the other hand, have a fantastic sense of smell and can detect water even in dry savannahs.

There are two species of wildebeest. The blue wildebeest and the black wildebeest. The blue wildebeest is the more common of the two and the only one to migrate. The black wildebeest is only found in Southern Africa and is territorial, preferring to stay in a particular location.

Kingfisher

There are 87 species of kingfisher. They can be divided into three major groups. River kingfishers, tree kingfishers, and water kingfishers. Most species of kingfisher are blue or green-colored with an orange or reddish-colored chest. The largest kingfisher in the world is Australia's laughing kookaburra, and the smallest is the African pygmy kingfisher.

Many of the world's kingfishers don't eat fish. Instead, they eat frogs, crustaceans, lizards, snakes, insects, and even any small mammals they can catch. Some kingfishers raid the nests of other birds to eat nestlings and eggs.

Kingfishers are cavity-nesting birds. Many species dig tunnels in soft banks, leading to small nesting chambers. Some kingfishers nest in tree cavities, and many forest-dwelling kingfishers nest in old, abandoned termite mounds. Both male and female kingfishers help to dig the nesting cavity, and both parents share incubation duties and care for their offspring together.

Zebra

There are three species of zebra. The Grévy's zebra, the mountain zebra, and the plains zebra. The plains zebra is by far the most common, but they can all be recognized by their distinctive black and white stripes. All zebras have black skin, so they are black animals with white stripes rather than white animals with black stripes.

Just like human fingerprints, each zebra's pattern of stripes is unique and can be used to identify individual animals. Researchers even use barcode guns with special 'zebra' software to identify individuals.

Their stripes provide protection against predators. Zebras live in large herds, and all the stripes confuse predators who can't choose which animal to hunt.

Some people think that a zebra's stripes help to cool the animals down. Hot air moves at different speeds over the black, light-absorbing stripes than it does over the white, light-reflecting stripes, so the zebra creates its own air currents.

The stripes definitely do provide camouflage to hide the zebras from predators. It might seem strange to humans that black and white acts as camouflage in a colorful setting, but lions, the zebras' main predator, are color blind.

A group of zebras can be called a dazzle or a zeal of zebras.

Heron

There are 64 different species of heron. They differ in size, color, and type of habitat. Herons can be found on every continent except Antarctica.

Herons prefer wetlands, swamps, coastlines, and areas near rivers, ponds, and lakes. Their plumage can be grey, white, brown, or black, depending on the species.

Herons are carnivores. They mainly eat fish, but their diet also includes frogs, small mammals, and birds, reptiles, and insects. Herons are active during the day and night. Their specially designed eyes allow them to see equally well at night and in the day.

Grey herons are the biggest birds most of us will see in our garden with a wingspan of about 6ft. The Goliath heron is the biggest heron with a wingspan of over 7ft.

Herons build their nests in tall trees so that the eggs are safe from predators on the ground.

<u>Beaver</u>

There are two species of beaver. The North American beaver and the European beaver. Although very similar in appearance and behavior, they are two separate species.

Beavers are best known for building dams, and they are perfectly at home in the water. They can remain underwater without breathing for up to 15 minutes and swim up to 5mph. One reason they build a dam is so that the lake behind it will grow deep enough that it doesn't completely freeze during the winter. Beavers then store food at the bottom of the unfrozen lake to eat during the cold months.

Beavers need very strong teeth to gnaw through all the trees they use to build their dams and their homes. Their tooth enamel contains iron, which makes their teeth strong and sharp but also orange. Because the orange enamel on the front of their teeth wears away more slowly than the white dentin on the back, beaver's teeth self-sharpen as they chew on trees.

Beaver homes, called lodges, are dome-like constructions built from branches and mud. They are built in open water for protection from predators and have underwater entrance holes.

Beavers use their broad, stiff tails like rudders to steer underwater, and for balance while sitting on land. They also use their tails to slap the water as a warning of danger or a warning to keep away. Beavers are the second-largest rodent in the world after the capybara.

Snake

Snakes live everywhere on Earth except Ireland, Iceland, New Zealand, and the North and South Poles. There are around 3,000 different species of snake, of which about 700 are venomous. The top 5 most venomous snakes in the world are the inland taipan, the eastern brown snake, the coastal taipan, the tiger snake, and the black tiger snake.

Most snakes live on land, but there are about 70 species of snakes that live in the Indian and Pacific oceans. These sea snakes are some of the most venomous snakes that exist, but they are little threat to humans because they're shy, gentle, and their fangs are too short to do much damage. There are even five species of flying snakes. Growing up to 4 feet long, some flying snakes can glide over 300 feet through the air.

The Black Mamba is the fastest snake in the world and can move up to 12mph. The biggest snake in the world is the reticulated python, which can grow up to 30 feet long. The smallest snakes in the world are Brahminy blind snakes, which are about 3 inches long. They are often mistaken for earthworms. The biggest venomous snake is the king cobra from Asia. It can grow up to 18 feet long and can inject enough venom to kill an elephant.

Snakes 'smell' with their forked tongue. They identify scents on their tongue using pits in the roof of their mouth called the Jacobson's organ. The two tips taste different amounts of chemicals in the air enabling snakes to 'smell in stereo' so they can tell which direction a smell, their prey, is coming from.

The amount of food a snake eats determines how many offspring it will have. The Arafura file snake eats the least and lays just one egg every decade. Snakes typically need to eat only 6-30 meals each year to be healthy.

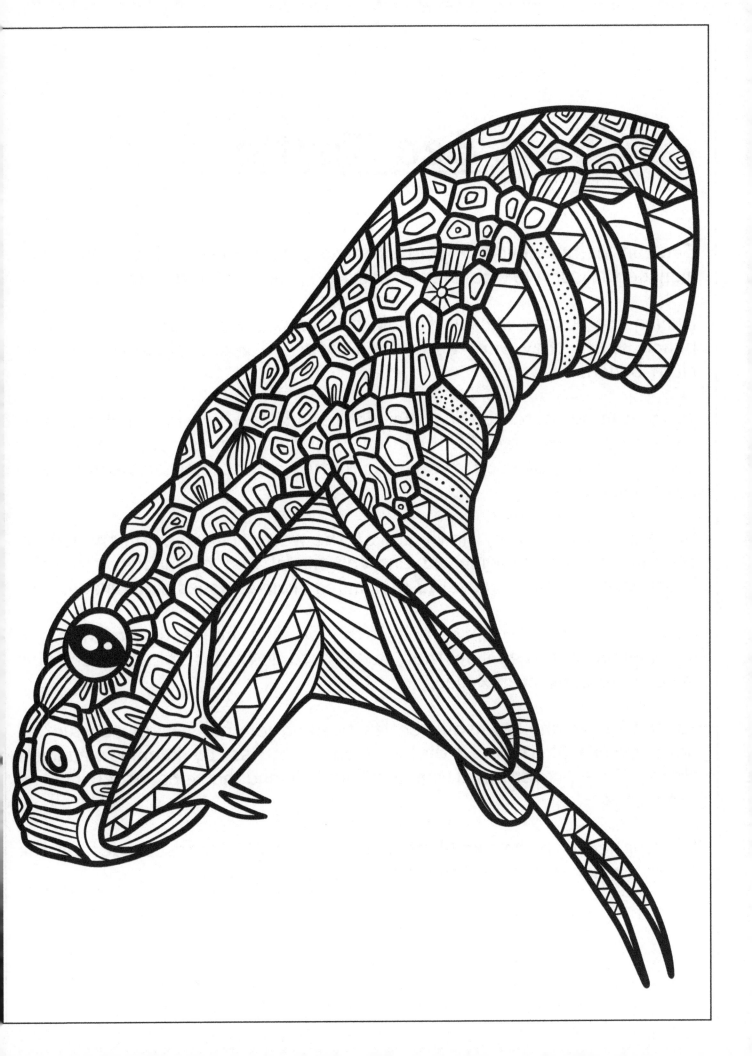

Sea Turtle

Sea turtles have lived on Earth for more than 220 million years. They managed to survive whatever it was that killed the dinosaurs.

During the nesting season, female turtles will return back to the same beach where they were born. Even after 30 years, they will find the right beach.

Young turtles hatch during the night, and they use moonlight to find their way to the sea. If there are too many lights coming from the beach or a nearby road, the young turtles can become disoriented and confused.

Sea turtles move very slowly out of the water. However, in the water, they are excellent swimmers and can travel vast distances with ease. Leatherback turtles travel 12,000 miles from Indonesia to Oregon.

Sea turtles can hold their breath for five hours underwater. To accomplish this, they slow their heart rate down to one beat every nine minutes to conserve oxygen.

Leatherbacks and hawksbill turtles feed on jellyfish. Green sea turtles have a more plant-based diet and eat seagrass. By keeping seagrass short, they prevent it from getting tall and harming other marine creatures.

Sea turtles have an excellent sense of direction and can detect the Earth's magnetic field, which they use as a compass.

Squirrel

Squirrels are rodents and can be categorized into three types: ground squirrels, tree squirrels, and flying squirrels. Flying squirrels can glide through the air due to flaps of skin that connect their limbs, providing a wing-like surface. They have been known to glide up to 300 feet.

There are around 280 different species of squirrel. The biggest species of squirrel is the Indian giant squirrel, which can grow up to 3 feet long. The smallest is the tiny African pygmy squirrel, which is only 4 inches long.

There are some very unique squirrels around the world. The tufted ground Squirrel, found only in Borneo, has a tale which is 130% the size of its body. The Kaibab squirrel has a pure white tail and only lives in the Grand Canyon Region of Arizona. The Indian palm squirrel has striking brown and white stripes which inspired a Hindu legend. It is said that a helpful squirrel was stroked by the deity Lord Rama, leaving behind finger-strokes down its back.

The arctic ground squirrel is the only warm-blooded mammal able to withstand body temperatures below freezing while hibernating.

Dugong

The dugong, also known as a sea cow, is a close relative of the manatee. Both groups of animals belong to the order Sirenia. Dugongs live in the warm coastal waters of the Red Sea, East Africa, Australia, Japan, and the Philippines. They can grow up to 11 feet long and weigh nearly a ton. It is thought that sightings of dugongs were the inspiration for tales of mermaids.

Dugongs have a flat tail and flippers like a whale, but they are more closely related to an elephant. They evolved 50 to 60 million years ago when an elephant-like creature entered the water. They are herbivores and eat seagrass. Each dugong can eat up to 90 pounds of seagrass a day.

Dugongs only come to the surface of the water to breathe, and unlike seals, they never come onto land. Most of the seagrass that these animals eat is found on the seafloor. To help them sink to the seafloor more quickly, Dugongs have evolved to have heavier, denser bones, so they use less energy when diving to the seabed.

Crab

Crabs are ancient. They first appeared on earth during the Jurassic period 200 million years ago.

There are more than 4,500 species of crabs. Crabs live in all the world's oceans, in freshwater, and on land. The Pea Crab is the smallest at about $\frac{1}{2}$ inch long. The Japanese Spider Crab is the largest measuring nearly 13 feet between its claws.

Crabs are decapods from the crustacean family. Decapod means 'ten-footed'. Crabs have 10 legs, but the first pair are its claws, which are called chelae.

A group of crabs is called a cast of crabs.

Honey Badger

The honey badger, also known as a ratel, is a carnivorous mammal that belongs to the weasel family. It has a reputation for being the most fearless and vicious of all mammals and lives in Africa and Asia, mainly in dry areas but also in forests and grasslands.

The honey badger has a very muscular body and strong legs. It has long, sharp claws that are used for attack, defense, and for digging holes in the ground. They also have an odd, very thick, loose-fitting skin. This makes it difficult for other animals to bite the honey badger. Their teeth can't puncture its skin, and when the honey badger feels their jaws snapping, it can swivel in its own skin to face its attacker and fight back.

To say the honey badger is an omnivore is an understatement. They will eat anything. Seriously, anything and everything. They will eat mammals, birds, reptiles, insects, larvae, plants, fruit, eggs, and roots.

Honey badgers get their name from their fondness for honey and honeybee larvae. They will seek out and attack honeybee hives with incredible determination, accepting hundreds of stings while they eat honey, honeycomb, and their favorite, the bee larvae, which is located at the center of the hive.

It's not just bee stings that the honey badger can tolerate. They can also tolerate bites from the world's deadliest snakes, like puff adders, mambas, and cobras, which they happily hunt, kill and eat.

They're not immune to venom, but their skin is so thick and sturdy that most bee stings and snake fangs cannot penetrate it.

If snake venom does get into its system, the honey badger can die, but often they just have a coma-like sleep while they recover.

Orangutan

Orangutans are giant, orange-colored apes and the only great ape that lives outside of Africa. There are 3 species of orangutan: the Bornean, the Sumatran, and a recently discovered new species, the Tapanuli. These critically endangered great apes are only found in the wild on the islands of Borneo and Sumatra.

Orangutans are one of mankind's closest relatives. Just like humans, they have 32 teeth, and their pregnancy lasts 9 months.

Orangutans are the largest arboreal (tree-dwelling) mammals, and they can move quickly from one branch to another. They are incredibly dexterous and use both hands and feet while gathering food and traveling through the trees. They can also hang by one arm for a long time while they eat.

They live in the trees to avoid predators like tigers or leopards that hunt on the ground. 50% of their diet consists of fruit. Other than that, orangutans like to eat leaves, bark, and insects. Every night they make themselves a new nest in the trees to sleep in.

Orangutans are highly intelligent animals. They will use tools like sticks to check the depth of water before crossing a river. They use branches to swat mosquitoes away, and when it rains or when the sun is too intense, they will use large leaves to protect their heads.

The name orangutan is a combination of two Indonesian words. 'Orang' meaning person and 'hutan' meaning forest. So orangutan means person of the forest.

Every day 25 orangutans die as their rainforest homes are cleared to make way for palm oil plantations.

Walrus

There are two subspecies of walrus: the north Pacific walrus and the North Atlantic walrus. Adult walruses can weigh up to $1\frac{1}{2}$ tons and reach 12 feet in length. They have grey to brown skin and a 6-inch layer of blubber, which keeps them warm. Both males and females have tusks.

Walruses have whiskers, called vibrissae, which they use to help find food along the bottom of the sea. Walruses eat mussels, clams, snails, worms, shrimps, sea cucumbers, and small fish. They can spend 30 minutes under the water hunting before returning to the surface to breathe and can eat up to 4,000 clams in one feeding.

Walruses live in large, noisy colonies that consist of tens to thousands of members. Walruses are very protective of each other. If one member is attacked by a predator, other animals will rush to help. Although large in size, walruses have two natural enemies: killer whales and polar bears.

When danger strikes, walruses are formidable fighters. Polar bears are among the few predators capable of successfully attacking a walrus, but even they tend to give fully-grown adults a wide berth. Agitated walruses have been documented repeatedly stabbing polar bears, causing severe injury or even death.

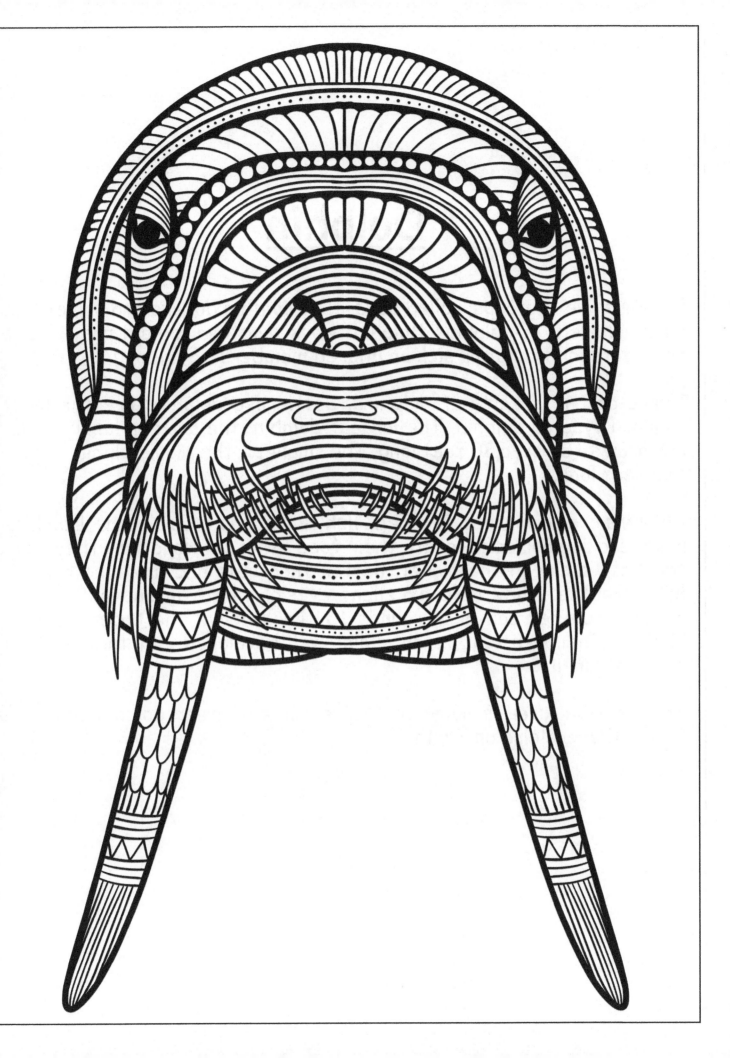

Dolphin

Dolphins live in groups, called pods, that contain dozens and sometimes even hundreds of dolphins. Dolphins work together to hunt prey, evade predators, and care for sick or injured members of the pod.

There are 40 species of dolphins. Bottlenose dolphins are the most common type of dolphin. The largest dolphin, the orca or killer whale, can grow to be over 30 feet long. The smallest, the Maui dolphin, is just five feet long.

Dolphins are carnivores. They eat fish, squid, and crustaceans. Dolphins make clicking noises to locate their food using echolocation. They have the best sonar on the planet, better than bats and anything humans have created. They have excellent eyesight both in and out of the water, and they can hear sounds 10 times above the upper limit of humans. Their sense of touch is also well developed, but they have no sense of smell.

The Amazon River is home to four species of river dolphin that are found nowhere else on Earth.

Koala

Koalas aren't bears, they aren't even related to bears, they are marsupials that are native to Australia. They only eat in eucalyptus leaves. There's so little nutrition in eucalyptus leaves that koalas spend up to 18 hours a day sleeping to conserve energy. Koalas are called koala bears because they look like a teddy bear.

Eucalyptus leaves provide all the moisture that koalas need, and they don't have to drink water. The word 'koala' is thought to mean 'no drink' or 'no water' in the Aboriginal language.

Koalas in the northern parts of Australia are smaller and have greyish fur. Those in southern parts of Australia are larger in size and have longer brownish fur.

Macaw

There are around 376 species of parrot throughout the world, and macaws are the biggest of all of them. The largest macaw, the Hyacinth macaw, has a huge wingspan of 5 feet.

Macaws are native to South and Central America and are found anywhere between Southern Mexico and Northern Argentina. They prefer rainforests, but can also be found in woodland and savannah habitats.

Once they reach breeding age at around 3 to 4 years old, macaws will pick a partner and stay with them for life. As partners, they spend a great deal of their time together, not only for breeding but also to share food, for grooming and in caring for their young. They can also be seen flying close to each other, almost touching, throughout the forest canopy.

Macaws are loud, and you will hear them before you see them. They are highly intelligent and gregarious birds that congregate in flocks of up to 100 individuals. These flocks are called a company or a pandemonium of macaws. Their loud calls, squawks, and other distinctive vocalizations can be heard throughout the jungle, especially in the early morning.

Macaws live for a long time, some birds reach 100 years of age.

Impala

Impalas are medium-sized antelopes and are members of the Bovidae family, they are related to goats, cattle, and sheep. They can be found only in Africa, and they live in grasslands, savannas, and on the edges of woodlands in South and East Africa. There are two species of Impala, the common impala, and the larger and darker black-faced impala. They grow to about 3 feet in height.

The impala is one of the most common African antelopes. Their main predators are lions, African hunting dogs, cheetahs, leopards, hyenas, and pythons. Impalas are known for their ability to leap great distances and quickly change direction when they are chased by predators. An impala can jump 10 feet vertically into the air and clear 33 feet horizontally when running all while running at speeds over 40mph.

Most young impalas are born around mid-day. This is the hottest and safest time of the day when most of their predators are resting. Half of newborn impalas are killed within the first few weeks of life.

Impalas migrate from high ground to lower ground according to the availability of suitable food. In the rainy season, when food is plentiful, they may gather in large herds of several hundred animals to graze.

Large herds offer protection from predators, such as lions. An alert impala will bark out an alarm that puts the entire herd to flight. If attacked, they scatter explosively in all directions. This sudden disorder makes it difficult for a predator to pick out and concentrate on a single target.

Llama

Llamas are members of the camelid family and closely related to the camel. Llamas come from South America, but today they can be found all around the world. They were domesticated thousands of years ago.

Llamas can be divided into two groups according to the length of their fur. Short coated (called Ccara) and the medium coated (called Curaca).

Llamas are strong, durable animals that can carry 30% of their body weight for long distances. They are used as pack animals in mountainous regions to transport goods. They also make excellent guards for livestock and will kick and spit at predators that are posing a threat.

Capybara

Capybaras are twice as big as beavers. They are only found in South American, and they are the largest rodents in the world. With an average weight of around 100 pounds, an adult capybara weighs nearly as much as an adult human.

Capybaras are herbivores. They eat aquatic plants, grasses, barks, tubers, and sugar cane. They like to be close to water, where they can escape from predators. Jaguars, anacondas, caimans, pumas, ocelots, and harpy eagles all love to eat capybaras.

Webbed feet help the capybaras to move in water, and their eyes and noses are on the top of their large heads to help them see and breathe while they swim.

Capybaras can stay underwater for up to 5 minutes at a time, and they often fall asleep in the water, which helps them to keep cool. They prefer to live in large groups of around 10-20 capybaras.

Gharial

The gharial is the only surviving member of the Gavialidae family of crocodile-like reptiles. It can be found in the fast-flowing rivers of northern India. Gharials were once numerous and widespread, but today there are only about 650 animals left in the wild. The gharial is classified as critically endangered.

Gharials can grow up to 15 feet in length and weigh 330 pounds, and they live for about 60 years. Mature males have a bulbous growth on their snout, which looks like an Indian pot called a ghara hence the name.

Gharials spend most of their time in the water. They only leave the water to bask in the sun and lay eggs on the sandy riverbanks.

Gharials are highly specialized predators and, although their snout looks odd, it is perfectly adapted to capture the gharial's favorite food, fish.

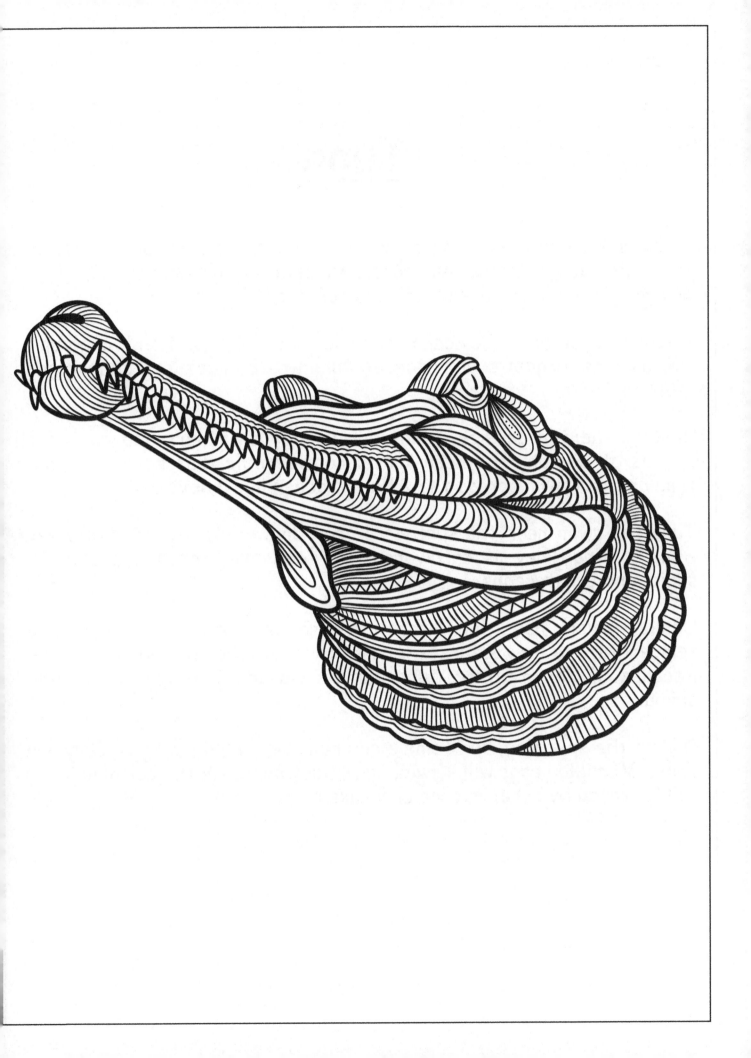

Tuna

There are 15 species of tuna, but the four most common are bluefin, yellowfin, skipjack, and albacore. All species of tuna are nomadic, swimming around the oceans looking for food.

Tuna are large fish. They can reach a length of 6.5 feet and weigh up to 500lbs. The largest ever recorded tuna was 21 feet long and weighed 1500lbs.

Despite their large size, tunas are speedy swimmers and can reach speeds of 62mph. They can travel considerable distances in a short time and can swim across the Atlantic ocean in 30 days at 16mph.

Tuna can swim near the surface or can dive to depths of 3,000 feet while hunting. They are carnivorous and feed on different types of fish, squid, and crustaceans.

Unlike other fish, tuna can increase and maintain their body temperature a few degrees above that of the surrounding water. Because of this feature, tuna can be classified as a warm-blooded animal.

During the spawning, one female can release 30 million eggs. Only 2 of those 30 million eggs will survive until adulthood. All the remaining eggs will be eaten by other marine creatures.

Aardvark

A fully grown Aardvark is about the size of a small pig. Roughly 6 feet long and weighing about 130 pounds, they are tough mammals that live throughout Sub-Saharan Africa. Their name comes from the Afrikaans word for 'earth pig.'

With their spade-shaped feet, they dig long burrows in which they raise their young and also shelter from the sun.

Aardvarks are nocturnal animals and travel up to 10 miles a night looking for ants and termites, which are their primary source of food. They have strong claws which they use to tear into termite mounds and dig up ants. They can eat 50,000 to 60,000 ants and termites each night, which they capture with their long, sticky tongue.

Aardvarks have poor eyesight but excellent hearing and a keen sense of smell. Like cats and dogs, they are digitigrades, meaning they walk on their toes, and not on the soles of their feet.

Aardvark is the first word in the English dictionary.

Lynx

The lynx is a member of the cat family. There are four species of lynx. The Spanish lynx, the Canadian lynx, the Eurasian lynx, and the bobcat. They can be found in Europe, Asia, and North America. The Eurasian lynx is the largest at about twice the size of an average house cat.

Lynx live in forested areas in the north and are well adapted to low temperatures. They have a thick coat of fur that changes color according to the season, and their feet are large and round, like snowshoes, to help them travel across deep snow.

Lynx are not particularly fast runners and rely on ambush to catch their prey. They are carnivores and hunt small mammals, such as snowshoe hare, mice, and squirrels, as well as birds. Some larger lynx will hunt bigger animals like deer.

The name lynx came from the Old English word lunx, meaning 'light, brightness,' which refers to their very bright, reflective eyes.

Lynx have tufts of black hair on the tips of their ears and a short or bobbed tail, which is why one species is called the bobcat.

Anteater

There are four species of anteaters. The giant anteater, the southern and northern tamanduas, and the silky anteaters. At about the size of a squirrel, the silky anteaters are the smallest while the giant anteater is the biggest at just over 6 feet long.

They catch their food with their long, sticky tongue, which is over 20 inches long and covered in tiny spines. Although they sleep for up to 15 hours a day, they can still eat up to 30,000 insects a day. The paws of all four species are tipped with enormous, knifelike claws so long and sharp that the anteaters have to walk on their knuckles or wrists to avoid stabbing themselves.

Giant anteaters can be found throughout South and Central America, and despite the name, their main diet is actually termites. They're also strong swimmers and have been known to swim down a river for miles in search of their next meal.

Manatee

Manatees look like walruses or small whales, but they are members of the sirenius family and are more closely related to elephants. Manatees, along with dugongs, are also known as sea cows. They are grey or grey-brown in color. There are three species of manatee. The Amazonian manatee, the West Indian or American manatee, and the African manatee. Their names indicate where they live.

Manatees can grow to 12 feet long and weigh more than 1000 pounds. Despite their gigantic size, they are elegant and agile in the water. They can swim up to 15mph, but they are usually much slower. So slow in fact that algae and barnacles can often be found growing on their backs.

Manatees have 2,000 thick, whisker-like hairs called vibrissae on their faces and 3,000 on their bodies, which they use to sense and explore the world around them. They are herbivores and need to eat around 100 pounds of vegetation a day.

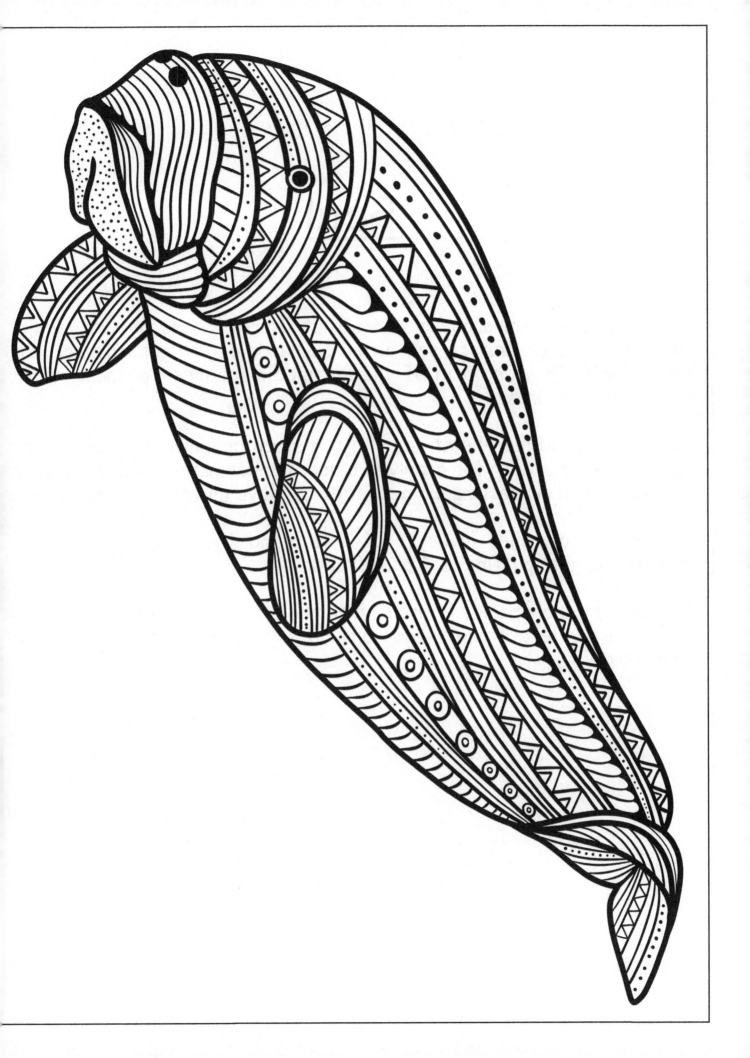

Seal

The seal is a carnivorous mammal that usually feeds on fish, squid, shellfish, crustaceans, or sea birds. Some, like the leopard seal, eat other seals. They are part of the Pinnipedia family of animals, which also includes walruses.

Seals can spend months at sea and can sleep underwater. Some seals can hold their breath for nearly two hours underwater by slowing their heartbeat and conserving oxygen. They can dive up to 3,000 feet down.

A female seal's milk is up to 50% fat, and their pups grow at an astonishing rate putting on 4 pounds a day.

The largest seal species is the southern elephant seal, which grows up to 19 feet in length and weighs around 4 tons, which is more than a rhinoceros.

Tortoise

Tortoises have been around for over 200 million years, which is longer than either lizards, birds, mammals, crocodiles or snakes.

Some tortoises can live to over 100 years old. Charles Darwin found and looked after a giant tortoise he called Harriet in 1835. She eventually died in an Australian zoo in 2006.

The scales on the outer shell of a tortoise are called scutes and are made of the same keratin as human fingernails. The growth rings around scutes can be counted to determine the approximate age of wild tortoises.

The color of their shell indicates where a tortoise comes from with lighter shells belonging to tortoises from warmer countries. The lightest known shade comes from the southern part of the Sahara Desert.

Tortoises have been further into space than any human being. In 1968, the Soviet Union's Zond 5 spacecraft was the first to circle the moon and return its tortoise passengers safely to Earth.

The largest tortoise species is the Galapagos tortoise. These giant tortoises hunt birds by luring them under their shells. They then drop and crush the birds beneath their weight.

A group of tortoises is called a creep of tortoises.

Crocodile

Crocodiles are large reptiles found in tropical regions of Africa, Asia, the Americas, and Australia. They are members of the order Crocodilia, which also includes caimans, gharials, and alligators.

Crocodiles have the strongest bite of any animal in the world. Most crocodiles live in freshwater rivers and lakes, but some live in saltwater. There are 16 species of crocodiles. The smallest crocodile is the dwarf crocodile. It grows to about 6 feet in length and weighs 13-15 pounds. The largest crocodile is the saltwater crocodile, which can grow up to 20 feet long and weigh a ton.

Saltwater crocodiles have a vast range covering northern Australia to eastern India and South-east Asia. They live in coastal habitats, but they are also comfortable in freshwater rivers. These huge reptiles are so well adapted to life in saltwater that they can spend days or even weeks at sea.

In the wild, crocodiles will clamp down on their prey with their huge jaws, crush it, and then swallow it whole. They cannot chew or break off small pieces of food like other animals.

To help with digestion, crocodiles swallow small stones that grind up the food in their stomachs. Thanks to their slow metabolisms, crocodiles can survive for months without food.

When a female crocodile lays her eggs, the temperature of the nest determines whether the babies will be boys or girls. If the temperature is less than 89°F, the baby crocodiles will be female. If it's above that temperature, they will be male.

Reindeer

Called reindeer in Europe, but caribou in North America, some scientists think that the reindeer was one of the first domesticated animals. Many Arctic societies still rely on this animal for food, clothing, and materials for shelter.

They are the only type of deer where both the male and female reindeers grow antlers. These antlers fall off and regrow every year.

Reindeer are found in Alaska, Canada, Greenland, northern Europe, and north Asia in tundra, mountains and woodland habitats. They feed, travel, and rest in herds of a few hundred animals. The herds often roam thousands of miles to find food in the winter. In spring, herds can join up to produce huge gatherings of up to half a million reindeer.

Reindeer are herbivores, and they eat herbs, ferns, mosses, grasses, fungi, and leaves. In the winter, reindeer must dig through the snow to find food. They dig using their antlers and eat a lichen called reindeer moss.

Wolverines, bears, and even eagles all prey on reindeer.

Reindeers get their name from the old Norse word 'hreinn,' meaning deer.

<u>Weasel</u>

Weasels are from the Mustelidae family and are in the same genus as polecats, ferrets, minks, and stoats. They might look cute, but they are expert killers. They have very fast metabolisms and need to eat about half their body weight every day. As a result, they've become fearsome hunters.

Weasels can be found in Britain, Western Europe, the Mediterranean, North Africa, North America, Asia, and New Zealand. They eat a wide variety of other animals, including rabbits, mice, voles, birds, frogs, and rats.

When food is plentiful, weasels will often kill much more than they can eat, but they dig underground caches near their den entrances and keep them stocked with leftovers. In the winter, when it's too cold to go outside, a weasel will just go to their cache and eat some leftovers.

Weasels are usually brown, grey, or black with white or yellowish markings. In the winter, though, all weasels become white.

Weasels will sometimes do a dance that researchers believe hypnotizes its prey so that it is temporarily off guard and then the weasel attacks.

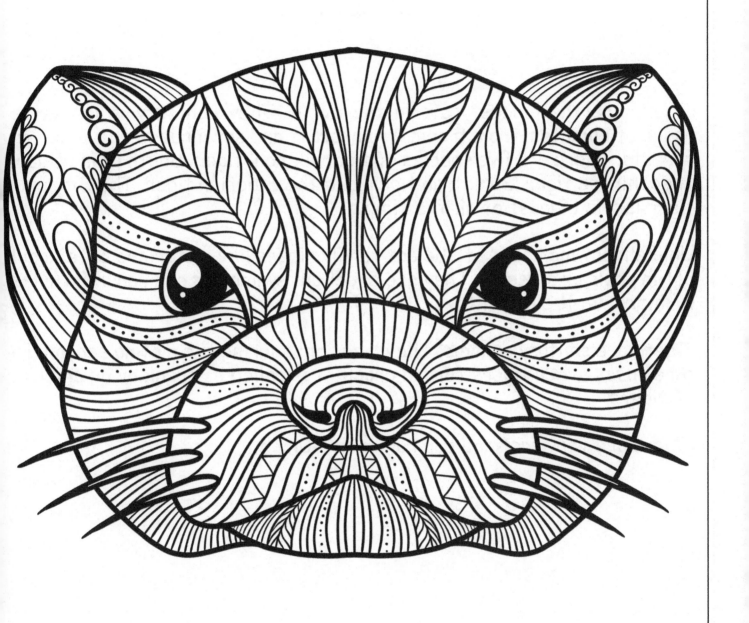

Tiger

Tigers are the biggest cats in the world. They can survive in a wide range of climates, from tropical rainforest and savannas to the Siberian forests. There are five species of tiger: Bengal tiger, South China tiger, Indochinese tiger, Sumatran tiger, and the Siberian tiger. The Siberian tiger is the biggest of all the tigers.

Unlike most members of the cat family tigers like water and often cool off in pools or streams. They are excellent swimmers and can swim miles with prey in their mouth.

Tigers are solitary animals. They meet only during the mating season. In rare cases, when tigers form a group, it is called a streak or an ambush of tigers.

Tigers are very fast and can run up to 40mph.

Eagle

Eagles can be divided broadly into four groups. Booted eagles, sea eagles, snake eagles, and giant forest eagles.

Booted eagles have a broad diet consisting of birds, small mammals, reptiles, rodents, amphibians, and insects.

Sea eagles or fish eagles feed mostly on fish.

Snake eagles specialize in capturing reptiles.

Giant forest eagles feed on forest animals. One of the largest forest eagles, the Harpy eagle, feeds on larger animals, including monkeys, sloths, and coatis.

Eagles are large, powerful birds of prey with a hooked beak, excellent eyesight, and powerful talons to help them catch prey. An eagle's eyesight is so good it can see prey up to two miles away.

Eagles build their nests called eyries on high cliffs or in tall trees. There are over 60 different species of eagle. The majority are found in Eurasia and Africa, with only 14 species found in other areas, including the Americas and Australia.

Hyena

Hyenas are not members of the dog or cat families. Instead, they are so unique that they have a family all their own, Hyaenidae.

The hyena is Africa's most common large carnivore. They have been on Earth for 24 million years and live in the savannas, grasslands, sub-deserts, and forests of Africa and Asia. There are four types of hyena: spotted, brown, striped, and the aardwolf.

The largest hyenas are the spotted hyenas, which are about 3 feet tall and weigh about 90lbs. The smallest is the aardwolves, which are about $1\frac{1}{2}$ feet tall and weigh about 60lbs.

Spotted hyenas hunt and kill about 95% of the animals they eat, while striped hyenas and brown hyenas are primarily scavengers. Aardwolves are insectivores, and they mainly eat termites.

A group of hyenas is called a cackle or a clan. A large cackle of hyenas can eat an entire zebra, including the bones, in under half an hour. A spotted hyena can eat up to one-third of its body weight in one meal.

Hyenas aren't particularly fast runners, but they can run for a long time. With a heart that is twice as large as that of similar-sized mammals, hyenas keep chasing their prey and tire them out before catching them.

Hummingbird

Hummingbirds are the smallest birds in the world. Most hummingbirds reach 3 inches in length and weigh no more than 1 ounce. The smallest hummingbird of all is the bee hummingbird, which is also the smallest bird of any kind, weighing less than $\frac{1}{10}$ of an ounce and measuring just nearly 2 inches in length. There are 343 different species of hummingbirds, and they only live in the Americas.

Hummingbirds have incredibly high heart rates. While flying, their heart beats 1200 times a minute, and they flap their wings 70 times a second. Unlike other birds, they flap their wings in a full circle, allowing them to hover, and they are the only birds that can fly backward. This type of flying requires a lot of energy, which is why hummingbirds eat a lot of high energy nectar every day. They also eat insects, which provide them with protein. They need to consume around half their own body weight every day.

Their metabolism is so high that every night hummingbirds have to enter a hibernation-like state called torpor, so they don't starve to death overnight. Torpor helps them preserve their energy. Their heart rate slows down, their temperature drops, and their metabolic rate decreases to just 7% of the normal. They usually hang upside-down in the tree during this phase.

Hummingbirds are also the smallest migrating bird. They don't migrate in flocks like other species. They usually travel alone for up to 500 miles at a time.

A flock of hummingbirds is known as a charm of hummingbirds.

<u>Iguana</u>

Iguanas are a type of large lizard. They can be found in Mexico, Central America, Brazil and in the Caribbean. There are 35 different iguana species, and different species live in different habitats. Some iguanas prefer tropical rainforests, some the water, and some live in desert conditions.

The longest iguana is the green iguana. It grows to between 5 and 7 feet long from nose to tail. The heaviest iguana is the blue iguana. It can weigh up to 30 pounds. The smallest iguana is the spiny-tailed iguana, which grows up to a maximum of 3 feet long.

Iguanas are herbivores. Some iguanas, such as the green iguana which live high in the trees of tropical rainforests, are folivores, which means that they just eat leaves.

The marine iguana of the Galápagos Islands scrapes algae off rocks on the seafloor for food. It is an excellent swimmer and can spend half an hour under the water looking for food before returning to the surface to breathe.

Bear

There are eight species of bear: American black bear, Asiatic black bear, brown bear, giant panda bear, polar bear, spectacled bear, sloth bear, and sun bear. Koala bears are not bears at all. They are marsupials and are not part of the bear family.

Most bears are omnivorous, but the giant panda only eats bamboo, and the polar bear is mostly carnivorous. Bears have excellent senses of smell, sight, and hearing. They can smell food, cubs, a mate, or predators from many miles away. Bears are also fantastic at climbing trees, swimming and can run at speeds of up to 37mph for short periods.

Bears are thought to be one of the most intelligent land animals. They have the largest and most complex brains in comparison to other land mammals their size. They are even known to cover their tracks to conceal themselves against hunters and are smart enough to roll rocks into bear traps to set off the trap and eat the bait in safety.

During hibernation, the bear's metabolism slows down, its body temperature decreases slightly, and its heart rate slows from a typical rate of 55 to just 9 beats per minute.

Baby bears are called cubs, female bears are called sows, and male bears are called boars. A group of bears is called a sloth of bears.

Yak

The yak is a close relative of buffalo and bison. 90% of all known yaks can be found on the Tibetan Plateau in the Himalayas. They are the third-largest beast in Asia, after elephants and rhinoceroses.

Yaks are the highest dwelling mammal in the world, typically living at altitudes of 18,000 feet and quite capable of living up to 23,600 feet above sea level. They can live at such high altitudes because they have enormous lungs allowing them to inhale lots of oxygen. Yaks are so well adapted to living at altitude that they struggle to live below 10,000 feet.

There are two species of yaks: domesticated and wild. Wild yaks have longer fur than domesticated yaks and can survive temperatures of -40°F. Domesticated yaks are highly valued for their fur, fatty milk, meat, and dung, which is used as a fuel. All yaks prefer cold temperatures and suffer from heat exhaustion in temperatures above 59°F.

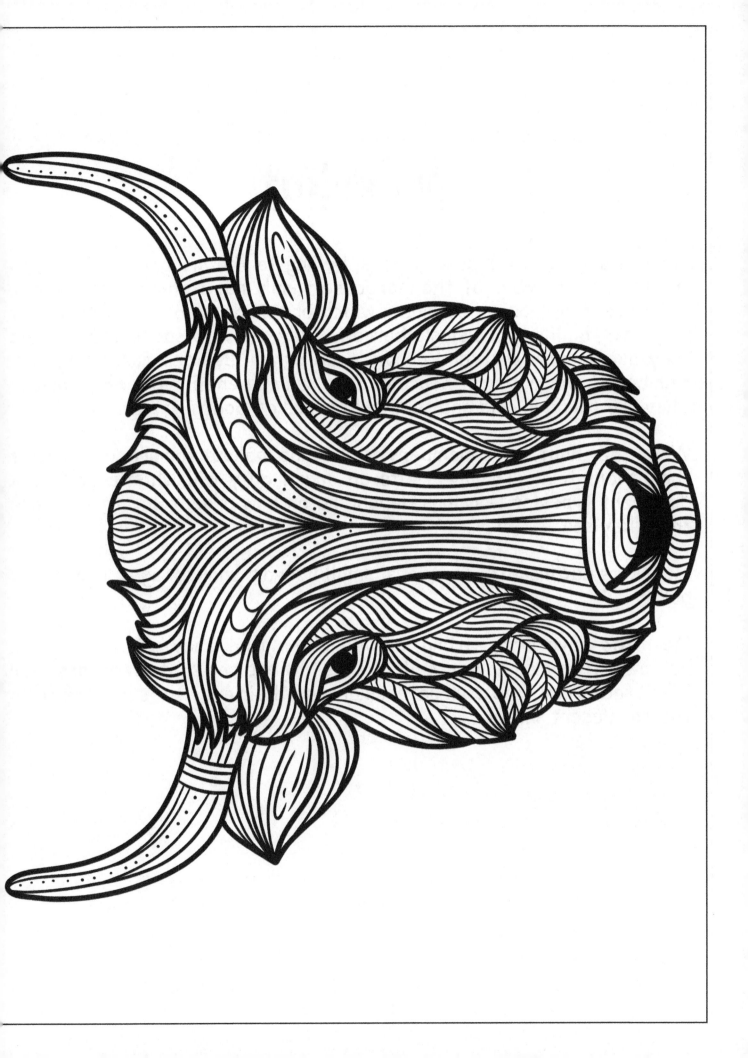

Meerkat

Meerkats, also known as suricates, belong to the mongoose family and are the only member of the mongoose family not to have a bushy tail. They live in groups called mobs, which are made up of 2-3 families of meerkats, all living in a single burrow. They are very social animals, and they like to play with and groom each other. Besides fun time, each member of the mob has their own duty, which benefits the whole group. They are found in arid and semi-arid areas of South Africa.

When they hunt, some members of the mob lookout for predators while the others hunt. The meerkats on guard duty will whistle and bark different types of warnings depending on how urgent any threats are that they see.

Meerkats eat insects, scorpions, small lizards, snakes, eggs, roots, and bulbs.

Meerkats have long, strong, curved claws that they use for digging burrows. They also have excellent eyesight and can spot predators over 1,500 feet away. The dark patches around their eyes cut sun glare from the hot desert surface.

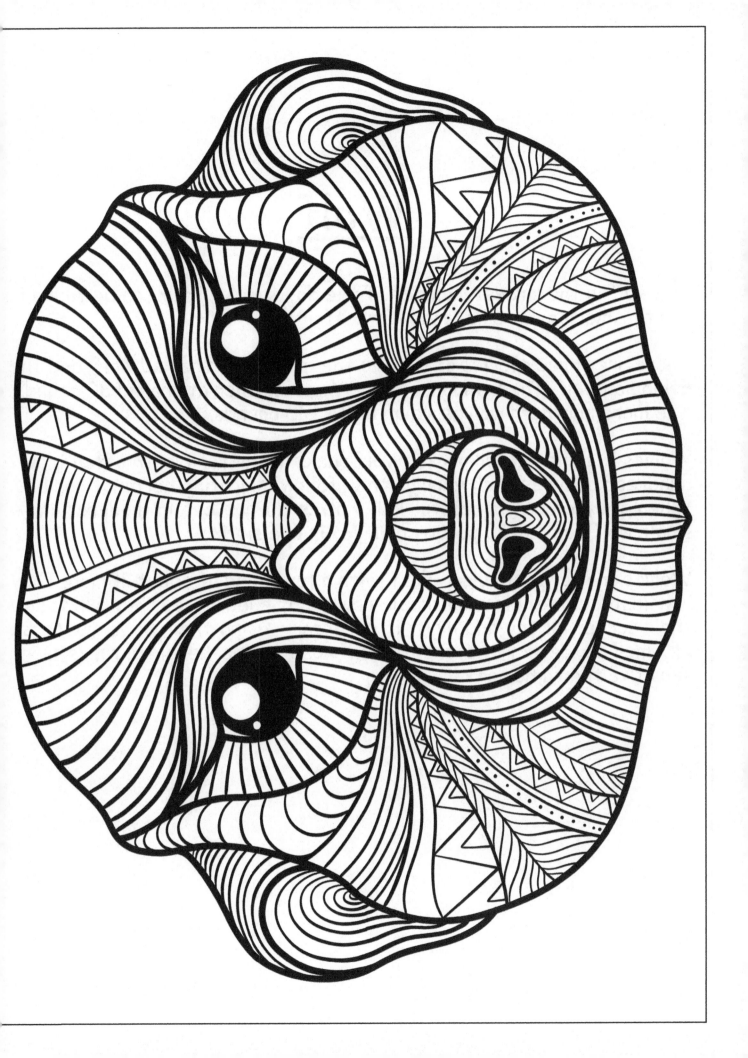

<u>Wolf</u>

The wolf is the largest member of the dog family. They can be found in North America, Eurasia, and North Africa.

There are three species of wolves: the grey wolf, the red wolf, and the Ethiopian wolf. The Ethiopian wolf is much smaller at around 30 pounds. The more northern wolves weigh up to 175 pounds.

Wolves live and hunt in packs. Wolf packs in the far North often travel hundreds of miles each year as they follow migrating herds of caribou. When they get a successful kill, wolves do not eat in moderation. A single wolf can eat 20 pounds of meat in one sitting.

Wolves are not particularly fast, with a top speed of about 28mph. They rely instead on their remarkable powers of endurance. They will follow their target all day and night if necessary, using their powerful sense of smell to detect the prey. Their nose is one hundred times more sensitive than a human's.

Thorny Devil

The thorny devil is also known as the thorny dragon or the mountain devil. It's a small, spiky lizard native to Australia.

They live in the arid scrubland and desert of the interior of the continent.

Thorny devils specialize in eating ants. They are what's known as obligate myrmecophages: they eat only ants. They can consume thousands of ants a day.

Thorny devils are 'sit-and-wait' predators. They sit near ant trails and wait for their prey to pass right in front of them, then use their sticky tongues to capture the ants.

Thorny devils are covered in densely-packed spikes, each no bigger than the thorns of a rose. These spikes are thought to make predators think twice before attempting to swallow a thorny devil. Thorny devils can also inflate their chests with air to make themselves bigger and harder for a predator to swallow.

Not only do their thorns protect them from predators, but they also help them get water in their arid habitat. There are hygroscopic (moisture-attracting) grooves between their thorns. They get water from the dew that condenses on their bodies overnight, during rare rainfalls, or by brushing up against dew-coated grass. Water in the grooves between their thorns is drawn by capillary action to their mouth. This allows the thorny dragon to suck water from all over its body.

They usually standstill when they believe there is a threat, but they can sprint away from predators if necessary. They have been recorded running up to 37mph.

Frog

There are over 5,000 frog species in the world. Each one has a unique call, and some frog calls can be heard a mile away. The biggest frog in the world is the Goliath frog. It lives in West Africa and can measure more than a foot in length and weigh over 6 pounds, which is as much as a newborn baby. The smallest frogs in the world are about $\frac{1}{2}$ inch long.

The wood frog of North America freezes in the winter and reanimates itself in the spring. When temperatures fall, the wood frog's body begins to shut down, and its breathing, heartbeat, and muscle movements stop. The water in the frog's cells is replaced with glucose and urea to prevent the cells from freezing and collapsing. When there's a thaw, the frog warms up, its body functions resume, and it hops off like nothing ever happened.

One type of desert frog, Australian water-holding frog, can wait as long as seven years for water by cocooning itself in a kind of transparent bag. The bag becomes its first meal once the rain comes.

The colorful skin of many tropical frogs acts as a warning to predators that these frogs are poisonous. One gram of the toxin produced by the skin of the golden poison dart frog could kill 100,000 people. It is thought to be one of the most poisonous animals on the planet.

A group of frogs can be called an army, a colony, or a knot of frogs.

Badger

Badgers live underground in burrows called setts. These setts can be over 150 feet long with a large room for sleeping in at the end. Badgers re-use their setts every year, and some setts are over 100 years old.

A male badger is called a boar, the female is a sow, and the babies are cubs. A group of badgers is called a clan (or sometimes a cete). Badgers belong to the Mustelidae family of animals, the same family as otters, ferrets, polecats, weasels, and wolverines.

There are 11 species of badger, grouped into 3 types. The Melinae (Eurasian badgers), Mellivorinae (Honey badger), and Taxideinae (American badger).

Badgers are nocturnal omnivores. They come out at night to feed on earthworms, young rabbits, mice, rats, voles, moles, hedgehogs, frogs, slugs, and snails. They will also eat most fruits, acorns, bulbs, oats, and wheat.

Badgers can run up to 19mph for short periods. They are also good at climbing and swimming.

<u>Camel</u>

There are 2 types of camel. The Dromedary (Arabic), which has one hump, and the Bactrian (Asian), which has two humps.

They are specially adapted to life in the desert. They have three eyelids and two rows of eyelashes to stop sand getting into their eyes. Their large two-toed feet, act like sandshoes to stop them from sinking into the sand.

They can survive without food and water for a long time. Most mammals would die of dehydration with 15% water loss, but camels can lose 20-25% without becoming dehydrated. When they do find water camels will drink as much as possible. They can drink up to 40 gallons of water at once.

Camels are famous for their humps. Most people think that the humps store water. They actually store fat, which the camel uses as a source of energy when other food sources are not available.

There are over 160 words for camel in Arabic.

Wolverine

The wolverine looks like a small bear, but it is actually the largest member of the weasel family. They live in the arctic and subarctic areas of North America, Canada, North Europe, Russia, and Siberia. There are two species of wolverine the European Wolverine and the North American Wolverine.

Wolverines have thick, dark, oily fur, which is hydrophobic, meaning water and frost won't stick to it. They are very quick and can run at speeds of up to 30mph. They do not hibernate and are well-adapted for living in the winter. They have dense fur, large paws that allow them to stay on top of deep snow, and crampon-like claws that enable them to climb up and over steep cliffs and snow-covered peaks.

The wolverine's scientific name, Gulo gulo, comes from the Latin word gulo, which means glutton, and they will eat anything. During the summer months, they will expand their diet with plants, berries, and roots, but mostly they live off rabbits, mice, porcupines, squirrels, and injured caribou. They will also scavenge off bears and are more than capable of driving a bear away from its catch.

Wolverines have a fantastic sense of smell and can detect a carcass lying 20 feet under the snow, allowing them to find the remains of animals killed in avalanches.

Wombat

Wombats are the second-largest marsupials in Australia after kangaroos, and they are the world's largest burrowing animal. Wombats prefer wet, forested areas and can be found in southeastern coastal regions of Australia and on the surrounding islands. There are three species of Wombats: Common, Northern Hairy-Nosed, and Southern Hairy-Nosed.; Their closest known relative is the koala.

Wombats are nocturnal animals that dig underground burrows for their homes. These tunnels can be over 100 feet long. They sleep in their burrow during the hot Australian day. When the temperature drops, wombats will leave their homes to start searching for food.

Wombats are herbivores, and their diet consists mainly of grass, roots, shrubs, moss, and bark. They are excellent swimmers and fast runners. They can run at 40mph, but only for short distances.

Unlike most marsupials, a wombat's pouch that they use to carry their young opens at the bottom rather than the top. This allows mother wombats to keep digging without scooping dirt onto their babies.

Their backward-facing pouch is not their only unique feature. Wombats have cube-shaped poop. They mark their territories with their poop, and the cube shape keeps it from rolling away. They will place a poop cube on fallen trees, fresh mushrooms, and rocks.

Whale Shark

The whale shark is the largest fish on the planet. It is called a whale shark because of its size and not because it is related to whales. Whale sharks live in the warm waters of the Pacific, Indian, and Atlantic Oceans.

Whale sharks are migratory species and change their location depending on the availability of food. The largest confirmed whale shark was 42 feet long and weighed 22 tons. They can live for up to 150 years.

Whale sharks are not fast swimmers. They are filter-feeders and drift through the water at 3mph straining vast amounts of water to feed on krill and plankton.

Parts of their skin are incredibly tough. Covered in hard, tooth-like scales called denticles, the hide on a whale shark's back can be up to 4 inches thick.

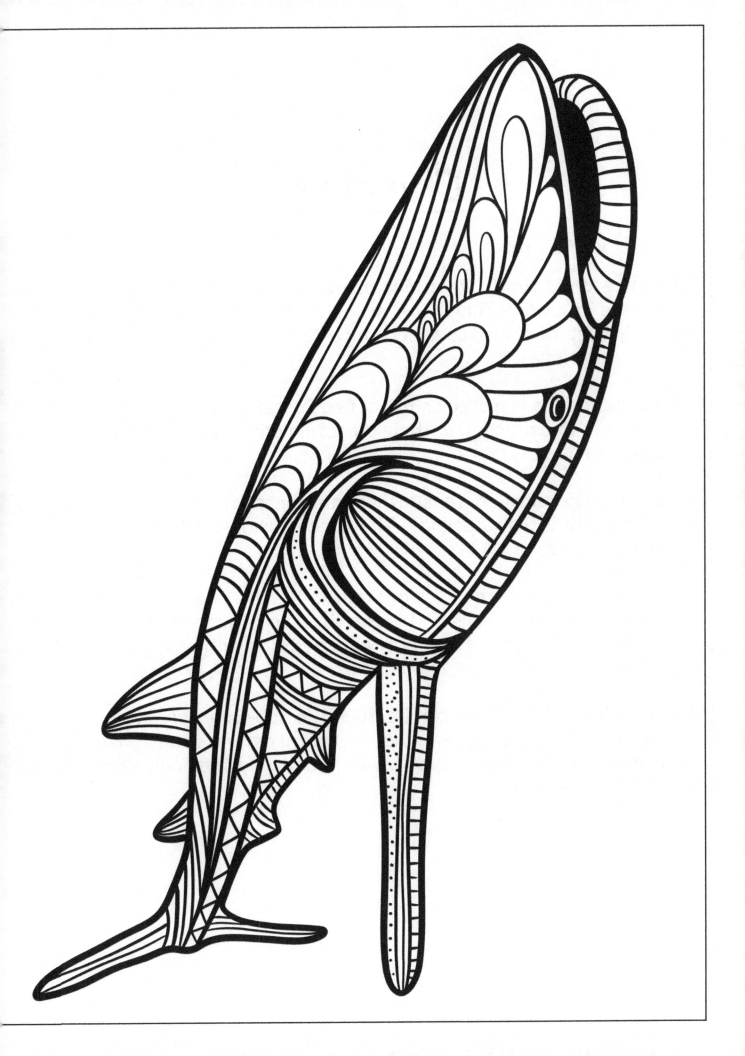

Cheetah

The cheetah is the fastest land animal in the world. They can reach a top speed of around 70mph in 3 seconds; however, they tire quickly and can only keep up their top speed for a few minutes before they are too tired to continue.

The cheetah's long muscular tail acts as a rudder when they're running. They use it to help control their direction and keep their balance when running at speed.

Cheetahs are smaller than other members of the big cat family, weighing only 100-130 pounds. They are considered to be the smallest of the big cats.

Cheetahs have fantastic eyesight during the day and can spot prey from 3 miles away. While lions and leopards usually hunt at night, cheetahs hunt during the day. They eat wildebeest, warthogs, birds, zebras, gazelles, deer, antelopes, and impalas.

Nearly all wild cheetahs can be found in sub-Saharan Africa. A small population of a few dozen lives in northeastern Iran. Cheetahs are considered a threatened species. It is believed that only about 12,000 are left in the wild.

Penguin

Penguins are flightless birds. They are very nearly exclusive to the southern hemisphere, but Galapagos penguins live right on the equator, and a few penguins drift into the northern hemisphere.

The Emperor Penguin is the tallest of all penguins standing 4 feet tall. The Little Blue Penguin is the smallest at only 1 foot tall.

A penguin's black and white plumage is excellent camouflage while swimming. The black feathers are hard to see from above, and the white feathers are hard to see from below.

Penguins can dive to depths of over 800 feet while hunting, although most dives are in the top 30 feet of water. The deepest dive ever recorded is by a female emperor penguin that dived to a depth of 1,800 feet. Emperor penguins can stay underwater for 20 minutes at a time.

The fastest species of penguin is the gentoo penguin, which can swim at up to 22mph.

A gathering of penguins is known as a huddle of penguins.

<u>Okapi</u>

The okapi is the only living relative of the giraffe. This beautiful animal lives in the Congo in Africa. Shy and usually solitary, the okapi is nearly impossible to see in the wild.

More commonly known as the 'forest giraffe,' okapis live in the rainforest. Their dark purple or reddish-brown fur, with white horizontal stripes on their front and hind legs, blends perfectly into the dense, damp vegetation. For many years, Europeans heard tales of the animal, but only the native dwellers of the Congo rainforest had actually seen it. As a result, the okapi became almost mythical and was known as the 'African unicorn.'

Giraffes and okapis are the only living species in the Giraffidae family and share several common features, such as elongated necks and long, dark tongues. An okapi's walk also closely resembles that of a giraffe. Both animals simultaneously step with the same front and hind leg on each side rather than moving alternate legs like other ungulates. Male okapis, like giraffes, also have short horns on their forehead that are covered in skin and called ossicones, which develop between one and five years of age.

To communicate with their calves in the dense forest, okapi mothers produce infrasonic (too low for human hearing) calls at around 14Hz.

Buffalo

True buffalo only live in Asia and Africa and the African buffalo is the only species of wild cattle to be found in Africa. It is also known as the Cape buffalo, forest buffalo, or savanna buffalo.

African buffalos are known for their excellent memory. They can recognize lions that have attacked the herd before and will preventively kill the cubs of those lions. They also have excellent eyesight and can spot a lion from over half a mile away.

Herds of African buffalos have a unique way of deciding which way to go. They vote on it. When the herd is ready to move on after resting, individuals stand up and face the direction in which they want to move. Eventually, when enough members have voted, the dominant female leads the herd off in the direction that most of the individuals have faced.

African buffalo are very aggressive and will attack humans. Every year over 200 people are killed by African buffalo. Buffalo are very protective of each other and take care of sick and old members of the herd, shielding them from predators. A herd is easily capable of driving away an entire pride of lions.

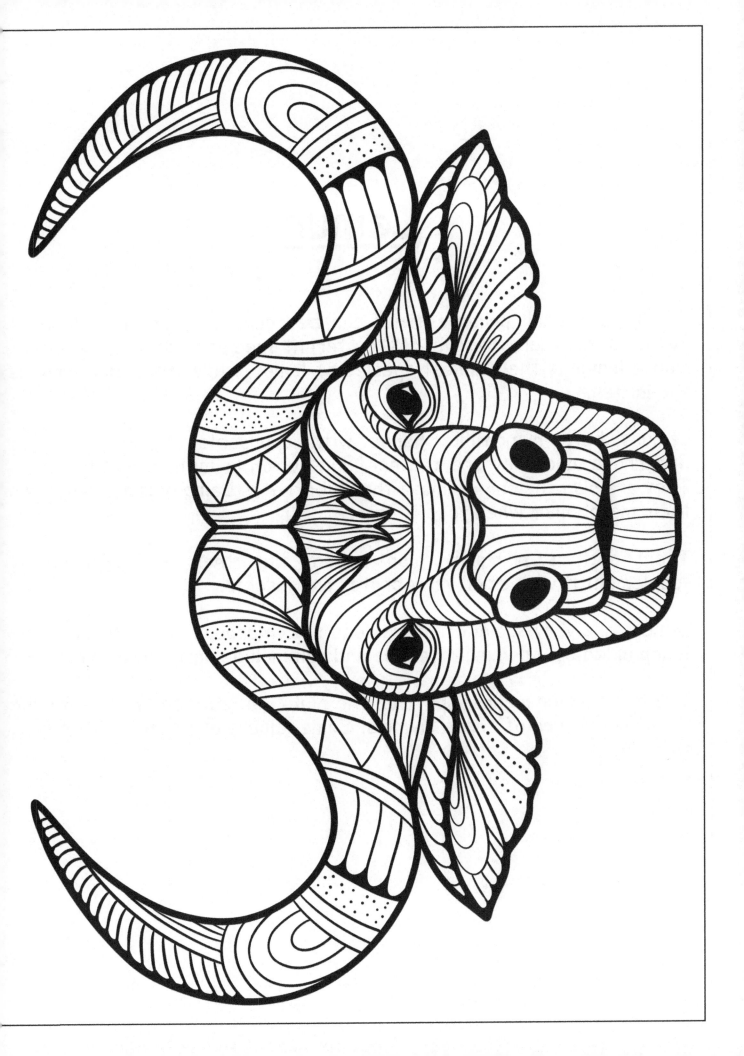

Lemur

Lemurs are small primates that can be found only on the island of Madagascar. There are over 100 different species of lemur. The dwarf mouse lemur is the smallest species of lemur, while the Indri lemur is the largest.

Lemurs have human-like hands with opposable thumbs and flat fingernails, and they are the only non-human primate with blue eyes. They are also the only primate that hibernates being able to slow down their metabolism when food is scarce.

Their diet is primarily plant-based, but they will occasionally supplement it with small vertebrates and insects.

Lemurs are very social creatures and live in groups called troops. The troop is led by a dominant female and can include up to 30 animals.

The name lemur means 'spirit of the night' in Latin and refers to the nocturnal nature of these animals. Some lemurs are also active during the day.

<u>Sloth</u>

There are two types of sloth, two-toed and three-toed. Confusingly both types have three toes on their rear legs. They should really be called two-fingered, and three-fingered sloths as the difference between them is found on their front limbs.

All sloths live in Central and South America. They prefer to live in dense rainforests where they spend most of their time living in the trees and sleeping up to 20 hours a day. They have evolved to be able to spend 90% of their time hanging upside down. Unlike other mammals, a sloth's internal organs are attached to its rib cage so that they don't press down on its lungs when the animal is upside down.

The sloth moves slower than any other mammal on the planet, generally traveling no more than 125 feet in a single day. On the rare occasions that they are on the ground, sloths only move at 1 foot per minute. Surprisingly though, they are excellent swimmers, traveling 3 times faster than they do on land. They even have a preferred stroke, the backstroke.

<u>Bonobo</u>

Bonobos are one of mankind's closest living relatives, sharing more than 98% of our DNA. They are closer genetically to us than they are to gorillas.

Initially, scientists thought the bonobo was just a smaller version of the common chimpanzee and called them pygmy chimpanzees.

The only country they are found in is the Democratic Republic of the Congo.

Bonobos are omnivores. They eat a variety of foods, including fruits, nuts, seeds, sprouts, vegetation, and mushrooms. They will also eat small mammals, insects, earthworms, honey, and eggs.

Bonobos live in a matriarchal society where the females dominate and make most of the decisions as far as group activities.

Hippopotamus

Hippopotamuses are the third largest land mammals and are famous for their bad temper. They are not afraid of humans and will attack anyone who enters their territory. Hippos are considered one of the most dangerous animals in Africa.

There are two types of hippos. The common hippo and the pygmy hippo. Common hippos are much larger animals. They can reach 12 feet in length and weigh up to 3 tons. Pygmy hippos reach about 6 feet in length and weigh up to 600 pounds.

A group of hippos is called a bloat of hippos and is made up of 10-30 animals.

Hippos spend most of their time in the water because they don't have sweat glands, and that is the only way they can keep cool. The name Hippopotamus comes from the Ancient Greek meaning river horse. Their closest living relatives are cetaceans (whales, porpoises, etc.) from which they diverged about 55 million years ago.

Hippos bask on the shoreline and secrete an oily red substance, which gave rise to the myth that they sweat blood. The liquid is actually a skin moistener and sunblock that may also provide protection against germs.

Underwater, an adult hippo needs to resurface every 5 minutes to breathe. The process of surfacing and breathing is automatic, and even a hippo sleeping underwater will rise and breathe without waking.

Lobster

Lobsters are crustaceans. 49 different lobster species can be found in the oceans all over the world. Depending on the species, lobsters vary in size from 1 to 3 feet in length. Most species are somewhere in between.

All lobsters can be divided into two groups: clawed and spiny. Clawed lobsters have claws, and they inhabit cold waters. Spiny lobsters have long antennas instead of claws, and they are found in warmer, tropical waters.

Clawed lobsters have claws of different sizes. The larger, crusher claw is used to catch and hold prey while the smaller, pincer claw is used for cutting and slicing prey.

Lobsters mainly eat fish, clams, crabs, starfish, and other sea life. They also consume algae and other types of sea vegetation.

Most lobsters are brown or olive-green in color, although some are bright blue in the wild. They all turn red when cooked, as that is the only pigment that isn't destroyed by the heat.

Wild lobsters can live for up to 100 years, but most lobsters live much shorter lives because they end up in lobster pots and then cooking pots. The largest lobster ever recorded weighed over 45 pounds and was 4ft long. It was thought to be at least 100 years old.

Lobsters are very sensitive to changes in the water temperature. They can travel enormous distances across the seafloor to move into better water. One lobster was recorded traveling over 200 miles. Sometimes lobsters will walk along holding claws. Usually, this is an older lobster leading a younger one.

Tapir

Tapirs are large mammals that look like pigs with prolonged snouts. They are found in Central and South America and Asia.

Tapirs live in swamps, grasslands, forests, and mountains. The closest relatives of tapirs are horses and rhinos.

Tapirs have been around for 20 million years, longer than many other mammals in the world, and have changed very little.

Adult tapirs aren't very colorful, but baby tapirs are covered in bright spots and stripes, which helps hide them in the underbrush from predators such as big cats.

Tapirs use their noses to grab fruit, leaves, and other food. They can stretch their nose up, to wrap around the food and pull it down to eat it. When threatened, tapirs will submerge themselves in rivers and use their snouts like a snorkel.

A group of tapirs is called a candle of tapirs.

Gorilla

Gorillas live in Central Africa. There are two main species of gorilla, the Eastern Gorilla, and the Western Gorilla. The Western Gorilla lives in West Africa in countries such as Cameroon, the Congo, the Central African Republic, and Gabon. The Eastern Gorilla lives in East Africa in countries such as Uganda and Rwanda.

Gorillas live in a range of habitats, from swamps to forests. There are lowland gorillas that live in bamboo forests, swamps, and forests. There are also mountain gorillas which live in forests in the mountains.

Eastern lowland gorillas, the biggest gorillas, can weigh up to 500 pounds, which is more than 3 people put together.

Gorilla families are called troops of gorillas. Gorillas usually stay in troops of around 10 individuals, with one silverback as the leader. Gorilla troops can be smaller or larger than this average, but they cannot have more than one silverback.

Humans share around 98% of their DNA with gorillas.

Pig

Pigs were the first animals to be domesticated, and there are 2 billion pigs in the world today. In Denmark, there are twice as many pigs as people.

The first book on pig farming was written by the Chinese Emperor Fo Hi in 3,468 BC. Historians think that pigs were domesticated even before then in around 6,000 BC.

Pigs are omnivores and will eat just about anything. Their sense of smell is 2,000 times more sensitive than ours. In Europe, pigs are trained to use their excellent sense of smell to search for truffles.

Pigs are louder than jet engines. They can scream at 130 decibels, drowning out the 120 decibels of a jet.

The British Prime Minister, Winston Churchill, famously said of pigs, 'I am fond of pigs. Dogs look up to us. Cats look down on us. Pigs treat us as equals.'

Red Panda

Despite their name, red pandas aren't related to giant pandas. They're more like skunks and raccoons. They can be found in the mountain forests of Nepal, India, Bhutan, China, Laos, and Myanmar.

Deforestation has significantly reduced their numbers, and the red panda is listed as an endangered species.

They are the size of a fox, and because of their red fir, they are also known as fire foxes. The red panda is the trademark of the Firefox web browser.

Just like giant pandas, red pandas have a 'thumb' which is used for grabbing bamboo. This thumb is a modified wrist bone. They spend most of their time in the trees eating bamboo, although they also eat fruit, roots, eggs, and small mammals.

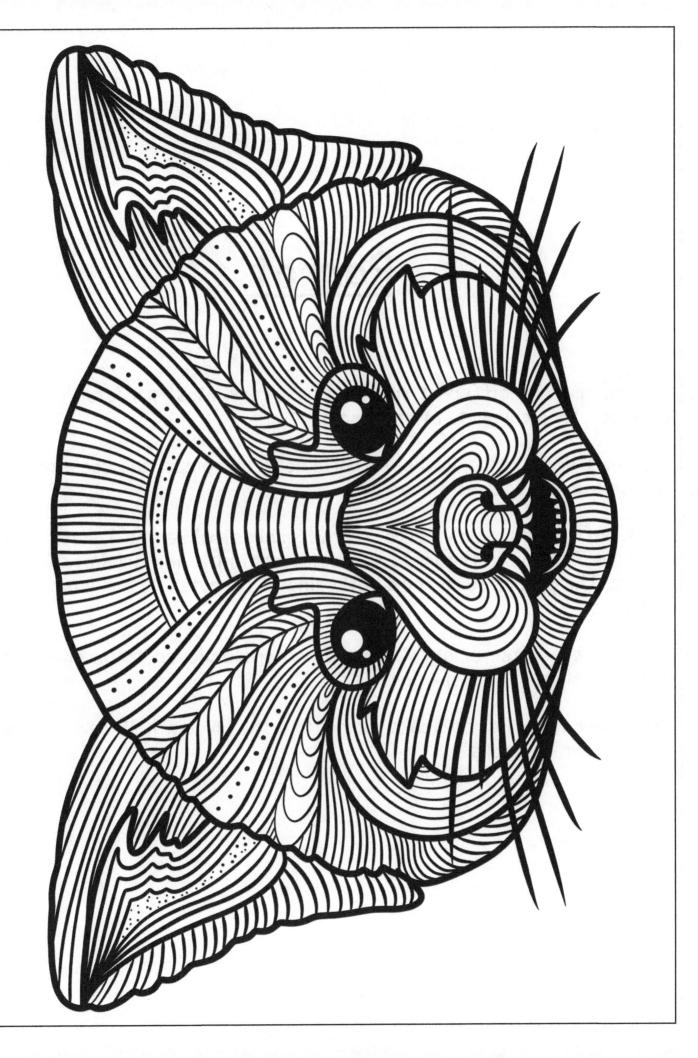

Parrot

There are 372 different species of parrots. Most parrots live in the warmer, tropical parts of the world.

Macaws, keas, kakas, lorikeets, parakeets, lovebirds, and cockatoos are all well-known species of parrots.

The buff-faced pygmy parrot is the smallest while the Kakapo parrot of New Zealand is the largest. Most parrots live in flocks of 20 to 30 birds. The proper term for a gathering of parrots is a pandemonium of parrots.

Parrots are often brightly colored and are believed to be one of the most intelligent bird species.

Parrots have powerful beaks. Some, like the Hyacinth Macaw, can even crack open coconuts.

Toucan

Toucans live in Northern parts of South America, the Caribbean, and Southern Mexico. There are around 40 different kinds of toucan, ranging in size from 6 inches to 24 inches. They have a long life expectancy living for up to 20 years in the wild.

Toucans are most well known for their enormous colorful beaks, which make up a third of the bird's total length. Despite its size, the beak is very light as it's made from keratin in a honeycomb structure. This does mean the toucan's beak is not very strong, so it can't be used for digging or fighting like other bird beaks.

Toucans use their beaks to keep cool. It is one of the best heat-regulating systems in the entire animal kingdom. Arteries in their bills expand when the bird gets hot and releases heat keeping the birds cool.

The relatively small wings of the toucan mean they are not very good at flying and cannot stay airborne for long. They often don't move far, and usually, hop between branches. Their colorful appearance is actually excellent camouflage for the rainforest, allowing them to hide amongst the South American plants.

Toucans live together in small flocks, and they make their nests in tree hollows that have often been created by their distant cousin, the woodpecker.

Leopard

The leopard is the most widespread of the 5 big cats.

Leopards are astoundingly strong. Pound for pound they are the strongest of the big cats. They spend much of their time in the trees and can haul prey heavier than themselves up into the trees to protect it from lions and hyenas.

Leopards are strong swimmers, agile jumpers, and fast runners. They have excellent eyesight and hearing, which helps them find prey at night time. They can see seven times better in the dark than humans.

Leopards hunt gazelles, antelopes, monkeys, snakes, warthogs, and porcupines.

The name leopard comes from the Greek word leopardus, which is a combination of leon (lion) and pardus (panther).

Leopards can be found all around the world, including Sub-Saharan Africa, northeast Africa, Central Asia, India, and China.

Ocean Sunfish

The ocean sunfish, also known as the common mola, looks like a colossal swimming head. In fact, the German name for a sunfish is Schwimmender Kopf, meaning 'swimming head.' The Polish name for sunfish is samogłów, or 'head alone.'

They spend up to half the day basking in the sun near the surface of the water. The average ocean sunfish is 10 feet long and weighs a ton, but the biggest can grow up to 5 tons. This makes them the world's largest bony fish.

Sunfish can lay up to 300,000,000 eggs at one time, more than any other vertebrate.

The sunfish's teeth are fused together in two plates that look like a parrot's beak. They feed mainly on jellyfish but will also eat sea sponges, small fish, squid, crustaceans, and brittle sea stars.

Their scientific name 'mola mola' comes from the Latin word for 'millstone.' Scientists used to think that sunfish weren't very inactive, spending their days sunbathing and feeding on jellyfish. New research has shown them to be voracious predators. They can dive up to 2,600 feet and travel several miles per day looking for food. After diving to the deepest, darkest parts of the ocean to hunt, Mola Mola spend half the day basking in the sun near the surface of the water to re-heat their bodies and aid digestion.

They have incredibly thick skin, up to 3 inches thick, and their closest relatives are the pufferfish and triggerfish.

Made in the USA
Las Vegas, NV
23 June 2022